SLAMMING:
THE UNAUTHORIZED CHANGE OF A CONSUMER'S TELEPHONE SERVICE PROVIDER

SLAMMING: THE UNAUTHORIZED CHANGE OF A CONSUMER'S TELEPHONE SERVICE PROVIDER

MATTHEW N. TERLAND
EDITOR

Nova Science Publishers, Inc.
New York

Copyright © 2006 by Nova Science Publishers, Inc.

All rights reserved. No part of this book may be reproduced, stored in a retrieval system or transmitted in any form or by any means: electronic, electrostatic, magnetic, tape, mechanical photocopying, recording or otherwise without the written permission of the Publisher.

For permission to use material from this book please contact us:
Telephone 631-231-7269; Fax 631-231-8175
Web Site: http://www.novapublishers.com

NOTICE TO THE READER

The Publisher has taken reasonable care in the preparation of this book, but makes no expressed or implied warranty of any kind and assumes no responsibility for any errors or omissions. No liability is assumed for incidental or consequential damages in connection with or arising out of information contained in this book. The Publisher shall not be liable for any special, consequential, or exemplary damages resulting, in whole or in part, from the readers' use of, or reliance upon, this material.

This publication is designed to provide accurate and authoritative information with regard to the subject matter covered herein. It is sold with the clear understanding that the Publisher is not engaged in rendering legal or any other professional services. If legal or any other expert assistance is required, the services of a competent person should be sought. FROM A DECLARATION OF PARTICIPANTS JOINTLY ADOPTED BY A COMMITTEE OF THE AMERICAN BAR ASSOCIATION AND A COMMITTEE OF PUBLISHERS.

LIBRARY OF CONGRESS CATALOGING-IN-PUBLICATION DATA

Available upon request

1-59454-760-2

Published by Nova Science Publishers, Inc. ✤ New York

CONTENTS

Preface		vii
Chapter 1	Slamming: The Unauthorized Change of a Consumer's Telephone Service Provider *Angele A. Gilroy*	1
Chapter 2	Telephone Bills: Charges on Local Telephone Bills *James R. Riehl*	25
Chapter 3	FCC Developments and FAQ Concerning Slamming *Federal Communications Commission*	61
Index		73

PREFACE

Changing a consumer's telephone service provider without his/her knowledge or consent is known as "slamming." This unauthorized change can occur for several reasons ranging from computer or human error to unscrupulous or illegal marketing practices. Regardless of the reason, slamming has a negative impact on both consumers and suppliers of telecommunications services. Despite existing regulations to prevent such practices and the overall condemnation of such activities, slamming is occurring with increasing frequency. According to data released by the Federal Communications Commission(FCC) 3,216 slamming complaints were filed in the first half of 2003. The issue of slamming is expected to continue as competition in the provision of intrastate long distance and local telecommunications services becomes more widespread. A significant level of consumer complaints, coupled with the potential for further abuses in an increasingly competitive market place, have prompted action to examine and strengthen deterrents to this practice. The FCC has been actively enforcing existing rules and continues to address outstanding slamming issues. The FCC, in a series of rulemakings, adopted rules that strengthen deterrents to slamming in compliance with provisions contained in the 1996 Telecommunications Act (P.L.104-104). All of these rules are now in effect. Under these revised rules, states are given the option of processing slamming complaints, and numerous states have chosen to do so. The telecommunications industry has condemned intentional slamming and is also taking steps to eliminate the practice. This new book examines this new rip-off practice.

Chapter 1

SLAMMING: THE UNAUTHORIZED CHANGE OF A CONSUMER'S TELEPHONE SERVICE PROVIDER[*]

Angele A. Gilroy

SUMMARY

Changing a consumer's telephone service provider without his/her knowledge or consent is known as "slamming." This unauthorized change can occur for several reasons ranging from computer or human error to unscrupulous or illegal marketing practices. Regardless of the reason, slamming has a negative impact on both consumers and suppliers of telecommunications services.

Despite existing regulations to prevent such practices and the overall condemnation of such activities, slamming is occurring with increasing frequency. According to data released by the Federal Communications Commission(FCC) 3,216 slamming complaints were filed in the first half of 2003. The issue of slamming is expected to continue as competition in the provision of intrastate long distance and local telecommunications services becomes more widespread.

---

[*] Excerpted from CRS Report IB98027 Reprted on October 8, 2003.

A significant level of consumer complaints, coupled with the potential for further abuses in an increasingly competitive marketplace, have prompted action to examine and strengthen deterrents to this practice. The FCC has been actively enforcing existing rules and continues to address outstanding slamming issues. The FCC, in a series of rulemakings, adopted rules that strengthen deterrents to slamming in compliance with provisions contained in the 1996 Telecommunications Act (P.L.104-104). All of these rules are now in effect. Under these revised rules, states are given the option of processing slamming complaints, and numerous states have chosen to do so. The telecommunications industry has condemned intentional slamming and is also taking steps to eliminate the practice.

Despite these activities, many members of Congress felt that additional legislation was needed to address this issue. The 105th Congress actively examined this issue, but adjourned without passing legislation. Two measures, S. 58 and S. 1084, introduced in the 106th Congress were not enacted. No legislation addressing slamming was introduced in the 107th Congress and none has been introduced in the 108th Congress, to date.

Although no one supports the practice of intentional slamming, some concerns have been expressed over the approaches being taken to curb this practice. One concern has focused on the necessity for, or specific provisions contained in, legislative measures, with the implementation of primary interexchange (long distance) carrier (PIC) freeze program among the most contentious. The FCC, on March 14, 2002, adopted a notice of proposed rulemaking to examine the charges imposed by local exchange carriers for PIC changes and adopted a further notice relating to third-party verifications procedures; action on both rulemakings are still pending. Another concern relevant to the slamming debate, that is the methodology used by the FCC to develop slamming statistics, also generated controversy.

Whether FCC-adopted slamming rules will be a sufficient deterrent to stop the practice of slamming, and negate congressional interest to enact legislation, remains to be seen.

MOST RECENT DEVELOPMENTS

The significant increase in the unauthorized change of a consumer's telephone service provider, a practice known as slamming, has prompted regulators, Members of Congress, and industry representatives to examine ways to protect consumers against this growing problem. The 105th Congress held several hearings and introduced many bills to address this issue, but adjourned without passing legislation. Two measures to further strengthen slamming regulations, S. 58, and S. 1084, were introduced in the 106th Congress, but neither was enacted. No legislation addressing slamming was introduced in the 107th Congress and none has been introduced in the 108th Congress, to date. Federal activity now rests with the FCC, as it attempts to enforce its rules to deter slamming. The FCC continues to take actions to enforce and further strengthen its slamming rules. The last of these new rules went into effect on November 28, 2000. Under these revised rules, states have the option of processing slamming complaints, and numerous states have opted to do so. On March 14, 2002, the FCC initiated a notice of proposed rulemaking to examine PIC-change charges; action is pending. A second further notice of proposed rulemaking, issued on March 17, 2003, imposing additional requirements on third-party verification services became effective on July 21, 2003. Whether Congress will feel that the implementation of current FCC rules negates the need for further legislative action remains unclear.

BACKGROUND AND ANALYSIS

Since the development of competition in the provision of long distance telecommunications services, consumers have been able to select the carrier of their choice, from among approximately 500 companies, to provide that service. However, an increasing number of consumers have that choice taken away from them when their designated telephone service provider is changed without their knowledge or consent. This unauthorized change can occur for several reasons, ranging from computer or human error to unscrupulous or illegal marketing practices. Regardless of the reason, this unauthorized switching, known as "slamming," has a negative impact on both the consumers and suppliers of telecommunications services. Consumers not only lose the right to subscribe to their carrier of choice; they may also be subject to lower quality of service, higher rates, or lose special features or premiums offered by their designated carrier. Consumers often do not realize they have been slammed until they find unfamiliar names or charges on their telephone bills. For some who do not examine their bills, such changes can go undetected for months or remain unnoticed indefinitely. Telecommunications carriers are also harmed by slamming, as this practice distorts the marketplace by increasing the customer base and revenues of the carrier that has illegally switched the consumer at the expense of the legitimately chosen carrier.

Despite existing regulations to prevent such practices and the overall condemnation of such activities, slamming continues to occur with significant frequency. According to data released by the Federal Communications Commission (FCC), slamming continues to be a major consumer concern, with 56,605 inquiries and 3,216 complaints filed in the first half of 2003. Since many consumers who are the victims of slamming may not file complaints, and over 50 million carrier selection changes are recorded each year, it is assumed that filed complaints represent a minority percentage of the actual problem. The potential for slamming is expected to increase as competition in the provision of intrastate long distance and local telecommunications services becomes more widespread.

A significant level of consumer complaints, coupled with the potential for further abuses in an increasingly competitive marketplace, has prompted action to examine and strengthen deterrents to this practice. How to prevent slamming is being addressed on several fronts. The FCC has revised its rules with an eye to strengthening its regulations and increasing penalties for violators. The 105th Congress while actively examining this issue, adjourned without passage of legislation. Similarly two measures (S. 58, S. 1084) introduced in the 106th Congress were not enacted. No legislation addressing slamming was introduced in the 107th Congress. The industry is attempting to self-regulate and has put forth proposals to stop this activity. (State regulatory bodies and legislatures, and law enforcement officials, are also taking actions to stop this practice. However, a review of state-level activities regarding slamming is beyond the scope of this issue brief.)

FEDERAL COMMUNICATIONS COMMISSION POLICIES

The FCC currently has policies and rules to protect consumers from the unauthorized switching of their long distance carriers, and it enforces them through the investigation of individual complaints. The FCC adopted its rules in response to the numerous complaints it received from state regulatory bodies, telecommunications carriers, and individual consumers. FCC rules currently require a long distance company to obtain a subscriber's authorization before a switch can occur. Authorization can be obtained in writing or can be confirmed orally. Specific requirements relating to what must be contained in written and oral authorizations are enumerated in the regulations. Furthermore, FCC rules protect consumers from paying potentially exorbitant rates. If a subscriber has been a victim of an unauthorized change, he/she is absolved of payment for up to 30 days; refunds of charges are set at 150 percent, split between the authorized carrier (100%) and the subscriber (50%). Carriers proven to be in violation of FCC rules are subject to fines and penalties. (See Telecommunications Act of 1996, for a discussion of the FCC's newly adopted more stringent regulations.)

From April 1994 to the end of 1999, the FCC imposed final forfeitures against 8 companies for $10.3 million, entered into consent decrees with 12 carriers with combined payments of $2.7 million and proposed $7.6 million in proposed notices of apparent liability against 5 companies. The FCC continues to take enforcement actions against violators. According to data compiled by the FCC in the past two years (2000-2001) its Enforcement Bureau has, through fines or consent decrees, taken action against 14 different carriers totaling over $16 million. In its first joint federal/state effort, the FCC, working with 13 states, filed on June 20, 2002, a $1.2 million fine against WebNet Communications Inc. of McLean, Va., for 20 alleged violations. In an April 21, 1998 action, the FCC levied its most severe penalty for slamming to date. For the first time, it revoked the operating authority of a telecommunications provider for slamming violations and levied a multi-million dollar fine. This action was taken against the Fletcher Companies, a group of long distance telephone companies, for engaging in slamming and numerous other violations of the Communications Act and FCC rules. These companies, and their principals, are barred from providing interstate telecommunications services without the prior consent of the FCC.

Furthermore, the FCC assessed forfeitures totaling $ 5.7 million but has never been able to collect. According to the FCC, it received more than 1,400 complaints against the Fletcher Companies, the majority of them filed from mid-1996 through 1997. Although these companies stopped providing services in 1997, during the FCC's investigation, this action was taken, according to the FCC, to ensure that none of these companies can resume operation and "engage in slamming or other conduct ... harmful to consumers."

Provisions contained in the Telecommunications Act of 1996 (see discussion below) expand the scope of the FCC's authority to address the problem of unauthorized switches. The FCC, in a December 17, 1998 order and subsequent reconsiderations (April 13, 2000 and July 21, 2000), expanded upon and adopted more stringent rules to combat slamming.

THE TELECOMMUNICATIONS ACT OF 1996 - NEW RULES TO COMBAT SLAMMING

The Telecommunications Act of 1996, which was signed into law on February 8, 1996 (P.L. 104-104), resulted in a major rewrite of the 1934 Communications Act (47 U.S.C. 151 et.seq.). Section 258 of the Telecommunications Act of 1996, which became Section 258 of the 1934 Communications Act, as amended, expands jurisdiction over, and creates a new penalty for, any telecommunications carrier that illegally changes a subscriber's designated telecommunications carrier.

Section 258 (a) prohibits telecommunications carriers from changing a subscriber's selection of both telephone exchange (local) and toll (long distance) service, unless the change complies with verification procedures prescribed by the FCC. The section expands the FCC's authority over such activity to include local as well as long distance service. State utility commissions are also permitted to enforce the procedures with respect to services within their state boundaries.

Section 258 (b) creates a new penalty, in addition to already existing penalties contained in law, for those who violate FCC verification procedures. Any telecommunications carrier that violates those procedures and collects charges for such service is required to pay the subscriber's properly designated carrier all the charges collected from that subscriber since the change occurred. The requirement would prevent violators from receiving financial rewards for the illegal switch. The FCC, in a December 17, 1998 action (CC Docket No. 94-129), adopted new regulations in compliance with the 1996 Act. These rules, with the exception of the liability provisions, went into effect in April 1999. (See: *Federal Register*, February 16, 1999, Vol. 64, No. 30, pp. 7746-7762.) The liability provisions were stayed by the D.C. Court of Appeals. On May 3, 2000 the FCC issued revised slamming liability rules (See: *Federal Register*, August 3, 2000, Vol. 65, No. 150, pp. 47687-47693.) which met court approval and the stay was lifted on June 27, 2000. These revised liability rules have since been enacted, taking effect on November 28, 2000. (See: *Federal Register*, November 8, 2000, Vol. 65, No. 217, p. 66934.)

The major provisions of these rules focus on three areas: consumer liability; verification methods; and consumer assistance.

Consumer Liability

The rules absolve slammed consumers of liability for charges incurred for the first 30-day period after an unauthorized switch. In cases where payment was made by the consumer, the unauthorized carrier must refund 150 percent of the charges to the authorized carrier. The authorized carrier is allowed to keep an amount equal to 100 percent of the consumer's bill with the remaining 50 percent returned to the consumer. Primary enforcement responsibility has been given to the states with the FCC assuming responsibility in those states unwilling or unable to undertake this role or if a complainant expressly indicates it wishes the FCC to resolve the matter. According to the FCC, 35 states, the District of Columbia, and Puerto Rico, have chosen to take on this responsibility.
(See [http://www.fcc.gov/slamming/states.html] for a listing of these states.)

Verification

Verification procedures used to confirm carrier switches are strengthened and extended to include a number of circumstances. There are a number of acceptable methods to verify changes, a consumer signature on an authorization paper form (i.e., a Letter of Agency; LOA), an electronic authorization (usually a customer initiated call to a toll-free number), a verification by an independent third party, and the more recently approved use of an Internet-based LOA (see Additional issues below). These verification methods are applied to both inbound calls (that is, calls initiated by consumers) as well as telemarketing calls initiated by carriers. Verification rules are also applied to changes in local as well as long distance carriers, but wireless carriers are exempt. The FCC has also applied verification procedures to the practice of implementing carrier freeze requests. In addition, the FCC rules require that solicitations for such freezes be clear and that the consumer be informed as to how such a freeze may be lifted. (See PIC Freeze Programs under Issues, below, for an explanation of this practice.)
The FCC also noted that these verification procedures do not preempt state law; these verification methods are to be used as a state minimum, but additional verification procedures may be adopted for intrastate carrier changes.

In a April 8, 2003 action (AT&T v. FCC, D.C. Cir., No. 01-1485, 4/8/03) the U.S. Court of Appeals for the District of Columbia found that the FCC exceeded its statutory authority in enforcing certain of its slamming rules relating to customer verification. While not remanding the FCC's rules the court did vacate fines totaling $80,000 imposed on AT&T. The FCC had imposed a fine on AT&T for slamming when, despite compliance with the FCC's procedures, an unauthorized person, without the knowledge of the line subscriber, authorized the switch. The court found that the FCC's requirement that the telecommunications carrier verify that the actual subscriber, and not just the person answering the line and claiming to have authority to authorize a carrier switch, authorize the switch exceeded the FCC's statutory authority. The court stated that the statue does not require actual authorization but only requires that the carrier get verification. Furthermore the court stated that the FCC's requirement that the carrier obtain "actual authorization" gives carriers "a virtually impossible task: guaranteeing that the person who answers the telephone is in fact authorized to make changes to that telephone line."

On March 17, 2003, the FCC issued a second further notice of proposed rulemaking (CC Docket 94-129; FCC 03-42) strengthening requirements on third-party verification procedures. These rules became effective July 21, 2003.

Consumer Assistance

New initiatives are established to ease the filing of consumer complaints and speed their resolution. These include the establishment of a web site to allow consumers to file complaints electronically and obtain on-line consumer protection information; the establishment of a toll-free number at the FCC to enable consumers to file complaints over the telephone; and the establishment of an electronic interface with carriers to improve industry response time and speed FCC resolution of complaints. The FCC, in conjunction with CC docket 98-170, has also adopted rules that establish truth-in-billing and billing format principles to enhance a consumer's ability to detect slamming. These rules establish requirements that, according to the FCC, are "intended to protect consumers against inaccurate and unfair billing practices."

Additional Issues

A number of issues not addressed in the April 13, 2000 reconsideration order were addressed in a subsequent FCC order adopted on July 21, 2000. These rules went into effect on April 2, 2001. These include: permitting the use of Internet LOAs in compliance with provisions contained in the E-Sign Act (P.L. 106-229), thereby allowing carrier changes to be made by consumers via the Internet; retaining the 3-way call as a verification method but requiring the carrier's sales representative to drop off the call once the connection has been established between the subscriber and the third party verifier; the institution of new complaint reporting requirements for carriers which require carriers to submit semiannual reports to the FCC's Enforcement Bureau containing, among other information, the number of slamming complaints theyhave received ; and adoption of carrier registration requirements that prevent slammers from evading detection simply by changing their names.

GENERAL ACCOUNTING OFFICE REPORTS

The General Accounting Office (GAO) at the request of Senator Collins, Chairman of the Permanent Subcommittee on Investigations, Committee on Government Affairs, undertook an investigation into the general issue of slamming, FCC and state regulatory efforts to curtail slamming, and a case study of the Fletcher Companies, a long distance provider that has come under regulatory scrutiny, and has since had its license revoked, for slamming complaints. This report, *Telephone Slamming and Its Harmful Effects*, was released in conjunction with testimony given at Subcommittee hearings on April 23, 1998. (For a full citation see For Additional Reading, below.)

Some of the major conclusions reached by the GAO, based on their three-month investigation into slamming practices and regulation, are as follows:

- Neither the FCC, the states, nor the telecommunications industry, have been effective in protecting the consumer from telephone slamming;
- Information provided by all long distance carriers in compliance with FCC-required tariff filing procedures, is not reviewed and is no deterrent to a slammer;

- Some states have taken significant action to protect consumers from slamming, but others have taken little action or have no antislamming regulations;
- The industry approach [to combat slamming] appears to be largely market-driven rather than consumer-oriented;
- Consumers and the industry itself are becoming increasingly vulnerable as targets for large scale fraud;
- Given [the present] environment, unscrupulous long-distance providers slam consumers, often with virtual impunity; and
- The most effective action that consumers can take to eliminate the chance of intentional slamming is to have their local exchange carrier freeze their choice of long distance providers."

The conclusions reached in the GAO report regarding FCC efforts to deter slamming, were discussed during hearings held, on April 23, 1998, by the Senate Permanent Investigations Subcommittee. Some subcommittee members expressed concern over the GAO's findings to FCC Chairman Kennard, who was called to testify at the hearing. Chairman Kennard defended the FCC's actions stating that the tariff filing procedure that was criticized by the GAO was not developed as a deterrent to slamming and that the FCC is currently working on new rules to strengthen existing policies to combat slamming. He also pointed to the severe punishment taken against Fletcher Companies to defend FCC actions. (See FCC policies, above.)

At the request of Senator Collins, the GAO undertook a second study examining the scope of and state and federal actions taken to combat abuses involving telephone services. The report, which was issued in July 1999, focused on two abuses, slamming and cramming. (Cramming is the practice of placing unauthorized charges for services and products on a consumer's telephone bill.) Among other things the report confirmed that, based on data from 1996 through 1998, "slamming continues to be a significant problem for consumers." This report, *State and Federal Actions to Curb Slamming and Cramming*, contains information on the number of complaints filed, state and federal regulations taken to protect consumers from such abuses, industry initiatives taken to curb these abuses, as well as state and federal enforcement actions taken against companies engaged in these practices. (For a full citation see For Additional Reading, below.)

CONGRESSIONAL ACTIVITY

Notwithstanding existing FCC rules and policies, and the passage of section 258 of the 1996 Telecommunications Act, some Members of Congress felt that additional legislative action needed to be taken to address slamming. The 105th Congress actively examined this issue, with each chamber passing its version of legislation to protect consumers against slamming. However, adjournment occurred before a final measure could be passed. Legislation to strengthen existing slamming regulations was introduced in the 106th Congress but was not enacted. No slamming measures were introduced in the 107th Congress and no measures have been introduced in the 108th Congress, to date. Whether the FCC's strengthened slamming rules will be a sufficient deterrent to stop the practice of slamming, and negate congressional interest to enact legislation remains unclear.

Action in the 106th Congress

Two measures, S. 58 and S. 1084, were introduced in the 106th Congress relating to the slamming issue. Sen. Susan Collins introduced the "Telephone Services Fraud Prevention and Enforcement Act of 1999" (S. 58), on January 19, 1999. While Senator Collins acknowledged recent FCC actions to strengthen its regulations to deter slamming as "... a step in the right direction" she felt that "... we need to do more to protect consumers..." against slamming. (S. 58 also addresses the practice of cramming. However the issue of cramming, that is the practice of placing unauthorized, misleading, or deceptive charges on consumer's telephone bills goes beyond the scope of this issue brief.) Senator McCain introduced the "Telecommunications Competition and Consumer Protection Act of 1999"(S. 1084) on May 19, 1999, one day after the court stay of FCC slamming liability rules. Citing the failure of the 105th Congress to pass slamming legislation, court action to stay FCC liability rules (which has since been lifted), and his objection to the industry-proposed third party administrator, Senator McCain offered a comprehensive measure "to better protect consumers."

S. 58

S. 58 attempted to further deter the practice of slamming by increasing consumer protections and strengthening enforcement at both the federal and state level. Included among the provisions to deter slamming contained in this measure were those that: required extensive and written notification and verification requirements when a subscriber switches long distance carriers; specified that Federal law *does not* preempt more restrictive state laws or regulations relating to slamming; authorized stiff penalties for those convicted of slamming including fines of not less than $40,000 for the first offense and not less than $100,000 for each subsequent offense. First time "willful violators" would have faced up to a year in prison for a first offense with repeat offenders up to 5 years. The bill extended FCC authority over violators beyond telecommunications carriers to include others such as billing agents; required local telephone companies to submit to the FCC, on a quarterly basis, a list of the number of slamming complaints received by service provider; allowed consumers to get refunds from unauthorized carriers; and protected consumer's rights to use the PIC freeze option. (See section on PIC Freeze Programs, below.) S. 58 was referred to the Senate Commerce, Science, and Transportation Committee where no further action was taken.

S. 1084
S. 1084 required the FCC, the Federal Trade Commission, and telecommunications carrier representatives to develop a code of practices to protect consumers from slamming. The code was required to contain, at a minimum, provisions that required companies to verify changes in a subscriber's service, restricted the use of "negative option marketing," required subscriber notification of any changes in service, and forbade the use of unfair and deceptive practices. Carriers were required to give subscribers who are victims of slamming credits for unauthorized charges and damages of $500. Adherence to the code would have been voluntary, but those carriers that chose not to follow the code would have been required to follow regulations prescribed by the FCC. Furthermore, the bill required the FCC to compile and publish a report, every 6 months, listing slamming violations by carrier. S. 1084 was referred to the Senate Commerce, Science, and Transportation Committee and received no further action.

Action in the 105th Congress

The 105th Congress held several hearings and introduced 11 bills (S. 1051, S. 1137, S. 1410, S. 1618, S. 1740, H.R. 2112, H.R. 2120, H.R. 3050, H.R. 3749, H.R. 3888, and H.R. 4176) to address this issue, but adjourned without passing legislation. S. 1618, the "Consumer Anti-Slamming Act," passed the Senate(99-0) with amendment, on May 12, 1998. H.R. 3888 passed the House, as amended, by voice vote, on October 12, 1998. Despite intense negotiations to resolve differences between the bills, the 105th Congress adjourned before H.R. 3888 could be brought to the Senate floor for consideration.

S. 1618

The "Consumer Anti-Slamming Act of 1998" (S. 1618), passed the Senate (99-0) with amendment, on May 12, 1998. This measure sought to combat the increase in slamming by strengthening safeguards to prevent slamming from occurring in the first place, establishing a process to resolve slamming complaints, and increasing the ability to punish those who are guilty of slamming. More specifically, the bill as passed by the Senate, prohibited long distance carriers and resellers (i.e., companies that lease excess capacity of established long distance carriers and then market those services) from changing a subscriber's long distance provider without the subscriber's explicit permission. (S. 1618 also applied to the unauthorized initiation of long distance service as well as unauthorized switching.) The local telephone company was prohibited from changing a consumer's long distance provider, unless the change is accompanied by a verbal, written, or electronic verification from the subscriber. Furthermore, the bill required that the verification be retained. The long distance company or reseller was required to send a written confirmation of the switch that includes the name of the new carrier, the date the switch was authorized, and the name of the person who authorized the switch, to the subscriber within 15 days. The use of negative option marketing, whereby a consumer must take some action to prevent a switch from occurring, was banned.

The bill also strengthened the complaint procedure byrequiring a companycharged with slamming to resolve the complaint within 120 days; absent resolution of the complaint, the company was required to give the consumer a copy of the retained verification, information about how to pursue the complaint with the FCC, and all other available remedies. Any company that ignored a consumer's complaint was to be subject to a penalty for slamming.

S. 1618 established both a complaint process at the FCC and minimum monetary penalties for offenders. The FCC was required to establish streamlined complaint resolution procedures and to issue a decision on slamming complaints within 150 days of filing. The FCC was given the authority to award both compensatory and punitive damages and was required to award those damages within 90 days of the liability determination. Minimum levels for fines were established, absent mitigating circumstances, with a fine of not less than $40,000 for first-time offenders and $150,000 for each subsequent offense. Individual subscribers could recover damages up to $500 from slammers and would not have had to pay the slamming carrier but could have elected to pay their designated carrier for those services. The FCC was given the authority to prosecute those who refuse to pay their fines. Those convicted of intentional slamming ("willful" slammers) would have been subject to criminal penalties and would have been prohibited from offering telecommunications services. Switchless resellers were required to post a bond with the FCC before they were able to offer long distance services, therebyassuring some degree of financial capabilityand that proceeds are available if slamming fines are levied. Furthermore, S. 1618 did not preclude or preempt state law or actions against slammers, and slamming victims were given the option of pursuing slamming complaints through the courts, instead of the FCC, through a state class action suit.

In an attempt to gather additional information on the incidence of and FCC action related to slamming, a number of reporting requirements were also included in the bill. Each telecommunications carrier or reseller was required to report slamming violations to the FCC on a quarterly basis to enable the FCC to identify those that engage in "patterns and practices" of slamming. The FCC was required to submit a report to Congress, by October 31, 1998, identifying the "top ten" carriers that were the subject of the most slamming complaints and the fines assessed by the FCC against all slamming violators in the previous year. (Calculation of the "top ten" was to be based on a ratio of the number of subscriber complaints to the total number of subscribers served.) The FCC was also directed to issue a report, within 180 days of the bill's enactment, on telemarketing practices used to solicit service provider changes by subscribers, and, if needed, initiate a rulemaking, within 120 days after the completion of its report, to prohibit undesirable practices. This report was also directed to study whether a third party should verify these changes and whether an independent third party should administer these changes.

H.R. 3888

The "Telecommunications Competition and Consumer Protection Act of 1998" (H.R. 3888), passed the House by voice vote, with amendment, on October 12, 1998. The House-passed measure contained a different approach from its Senate counterpart to combat slamming. H.R. 3888 called for the establishment of a voluntary code of conduct as an alternative to FCC regulation to address the issue. Failure to comply with or withdrawal from the voluntary code would result in a carrier being subject to FCC regulation. The FCC was required, within 180 days of enactment, to establish after consultation with the Federal Trade Commission, state commissions, industry representatives and consumers, a voluntary code of "Subscriber Protection Practices" governing changes in a subscriber's telephone exchange and/or toll services. The bill enumerated minimum standards to be addressed in the voluntary code, including those dealing with notification, verification, and marketing. Guidelines relating to liability, reimbursements, record keeping, and independent audits were also included. The FCC was required to review the code every 2 years to ensure that its requirements "adequately protect consumers." Each carrier was given 10 days within adoption of the code, or commencement of operation, to elect to comply with the voluntary code. Those telecommunications carriers, including resellers, that elected not to comply with the voluntary code, withdrew from such election, or had such election revoked by the FCC, were to be subject to presumably more stringent FCC regulations.

H.R. 3888 also detailed specific, more stringent, minimum requirements to be incorporated into FCC- developed regulations for carriers not operating under the voluntary code. The FCC was also required to compile and a publish a report, on a semiannual basis, ranking carriers by the percentage of verified complaints, excluding those generated by the carrier's unaffiliated resellers, compared to the number of changes. Carriers listed among the 5 worst performers (based upon the percentage of verified complaints compared to its number of carrier selection changes) in the semiannual reports for three consecutive times were to be subject to FCC investigation. Carriers found in violation of the voluntary code or found willfully and repeatedly slamming were subject to a fine of up to $1 million.

Additional provisions in the bill included those that: gave subscribers credit for charges incurred when using the slamming carrier's service; gave state attorneys general enforcement authority under the federal legislation; upheld any state laws regarding slamming that were **less** restrictive than those imposed under this bill; and directed the Commerce Department's National Telecommunications and Information Administration to report to Congress on "the feasibility and desirability" of establishing a neutral third party to administer a system to prevent slamming.

The version of H.R. 3888 passed by the House Commerce Committee, and ultimately the full House, was significantly different from the subcommittee-passed H.R. 3888 which was more aligned with the Senate-passed measure. As a result, the House passed H.R. 3888 contained a significantlydifferent approach to combat slamming from its Senate counterpart, S. 1618. Negotiations between the House and Senate to reconcile differences between the two measures continued through the waning days of the session. Despite such efforts, however, H.R. 3888 was not brought to the Senate floor and legislation to address slamming was not enacted prior to the adjournment of the 105th Congress.

INDUSTRY INITIATIVES

The telecommunications industry has acknowledged the existence of a slamming problem but is not necessarily in agreement with an approach to solve it. The Competitive Telecommunications Association (CompTel), a telecommunications trade association that represents competitive telecommunications service providers, issued a statement that called for "zero tolerance" of intentional slamming but that stressed industry self-policing. CompTel urged carriers to agree to investigate all slamming allegations, repay consumers who have been the victims of slamming, and terminate any employees or agents who "knowingly and willfully engaged in such practices." The statement also advocated uniformity in state and federal slamming requirements, to lessen consumer confusion, and called for the levying of fines, but solely in cases where it has be proven that the carrier "has engaged in willful and intentional slamming...."

ISSUES

Although no one supports the practice of intentional slamming, some concerns have been expressed over the approaches being taken to curb this practice. One concern has focused on the necessity for, or concern over specific provisions contained in, recent legislative proposals. Two other concerns addressed in pending legislation, have also generated controversy: the implementation of primary interexchange carrier (PIC) freeze programs; and the methodology used by the FCC to develop slamming statistics.

Legislation

Some favor voluntary private-sector initiatives to combat slamming rather than the enactment of legislation. They point to recent industry initiatives, such as the ones discussed above, to support that position. Others support vigorous enforcement of current FCC regulations and continued consumer education to combat the increase in slamming complaints. The enactment of additional legislative measures prescribing new regulations is seen, by some, as an action that is premature and that should be taken only as a last resort if the slamming problem continues. Many take the position that no further legislative action should be taken until the impact of recently adopted FCC regulations can be assessed.

Others support the enactment of legislation. They cite the trend of the rise in slamming complaints despite existing FCC regulations, as proof that additional legislative action is needed. The extent and growth of the existing problem, coupled with the potential for further abuse, make it necessary, supporters claim, to enact legislation to curb slamming. The release of a GAO report critical of current FCC efforts to reduce the occurrence of slamming gave supporters of legislation additional impetus in the 105th and 106th Congresses. (See GAO Report, above.) It is up to the Congress, they state, to establish through law stronger measures and increased penalties to protect both consumers and suppliers of telecommunications services from slamming. Those in favor of enactment of legislation also state that FCC regulations directly supported by statute, versus FCC developed policies, are less susceptible to change and will better withstand scrutiny if challenged in the courts. The May 18, 1999 U.S. Appeals Court stay of the liability provisions of the FCC's slamming rules is cited as further proof in support of the need for enactment of legislation.

Those supporting legislative action, however, are not necessarily united in the approach such legislation should take. Some have expressed concern over the breath of the proposed regulations contained in the measures that were considered in the 105th and 106th Congresses and/or individual provisions contained within them. Concern has been voiced by some that the consumer protections that were proposed were too extensive and may be overly burdensome and costly for smaller carriers attempting to compete with the major long distance carriers. Mandatory third party verification is cited as an example of a proposal that would be costly for small carriers to implement. Proposals to require switchless resellers to post a "surety bond" with the FCC to pay for possible fines or penalties also came under criticism. The Telecommunications Resellers Association claims that such a provision not only discriminates against switchless resellers, who are small businesses, but would also cause an "anticompetitive effect" in the marketplace by decreasing consumer choice. Additional concern has also been expressed over the content of other provisions contained in other measures. Provisions, such as ones that give full reimbursement to consumers if they are slammed, instead of solely reimbursement of the overcharge, have generated concerns that it might possibly lead to consumers fraudulently claiming they have been slammed, to avoid paying any charges for long distance calls. Proposals to require slammers to pay fines to consumers they harm could result in the creation of the "wrong incentive structure..." according to AT&T, by rewarding people who have been slammed instead of trying to discipline those who do the slamming. Furthermore, some have expressed concerns that fines and punishments not be levied against the long distance carrier in all cases, since in some instances unwanted switches can be attributed to the local exchange carrier responsible for executing the switch. On the other hand, local exchange carriers have expressed some concerns that they should not be held liable for solely executing a change since short of confirming each switch, they cannot insure that each change is authorized by the consumer.

PIC Freeze Programs

One practice currently used to prevent slamming is the freezing of a customer's primary interexchange (long distance) carrier, or PIC. The PIC freeze is implemented by the local exchange carrier at the request of the customer, and prohibits the switch of the customer's designated long distance carrier without his/her express approval. In that way slamming is prevented, since the customer's long distance carrier cannot be changed without express permission. While most see the PIC freeze as a viable option to prevent slamming in the long distance market, some concerns have been expressed over the potential for misuse of this option. Some see the potential for the PIC freeze to inhibit competition, if the means required to lift the freeze are perceived by the consumer as too burdensome or the charges to implement the change are excessive. The FCC, in a March 14, 2002 action, has initiated a notice of proposed rulemaking (CC Docket No. 02-53) to address a petition, filed by the Competitive Telecommunications Association, regarding charges levied by ILECs for changing PICs for end users. The Competitive Telecommunications Association feels that the present $5 PIC change charge safe harbor exceeds actual cost and hampers competition. Upon its initiation of the inquiry, the FCC concluded that "significant industry and market changes have occurred since the implementation of the safe harbor in 1984" and sought comment on FCC policies for regulating PIC change charges. Comments were due June 14, 2002 and reply comments were due July 1, 2002. The possible misuse of the PIC freeze through the implementation of an illegal or unauthorized PIC freeze by the customer's local exchange carrier, absent the customer's authorization, has also been raised. The extension of the PIC freeze option, beyond the designation of the long distance carrier, to cover the designation of local exchange and intrastate long distance (toll call) carriers, has also raised significant concerns. Some see the expanded use of the PIC freeze option as unnecessary and feel that the PIC freeze is being misused to protect the local exchange carriers market share in the face of growing competition. As incumbent local exchange carriers face increasing competition in the local exchange market and seek to offer long distance service within their service territories, some feel that the potential for abuse of the PIC freeze will become greater. Some support the elimination of local exchange carrier control over the processing of all carrier changes and freezes, and favor the establishment of an independent third party to administer and execute such changes.

Local exchange carriers defend the use of the PIC freeze, arguing that it is an appropriate method to protect consumers against the growing problem of slamming. They assert that there have been no widespread complaints about the manner in which the PIC freeze is implemented and note that the FCC has encouraged carriers to take steps to help prevent slamming. They also state that the manner in which the program is implemented varies from carrier to carrier and that many of the potential and perceived abuses, such as high charges or difficultly in switching, do not apply to most programs. Furthermore, many local exchange carriers claim that they do not actively market the PIC freeze option but only offer it in response to customers who complain about slamming or who specifically inquire about it.

Slamming Statistics

The methodology used by the FCC to develop slamming statistics has also been brought under question. The manner in which the FCC calculates and interprets its slamming statistics has significant ramifications, as several legislative measures required the FCC to report such information to Congress on an annual basis.

The GAO has criticized the methodology used by the FCC to determine the list of top slamming offenders, a list that is published annually by the FCC in its *Common Carrier Scorecard.* The FCC compares slamming offenders by citing the ratio of the number of complaints per million dollars of company revenue. That methodology, according to the GAO, is flawed because it can lead to a severe understatement of the revenue-to-complaint ratio for the smaller companies, or resellers. This occurs, according the GAO, because resellers are not required to, and generally do not, report their revenue to the FCC unless the revenue exceeds $109 million. To enable the FCC to make comparisons, to list the top slamming offenders, the FCC assumes that those resellers that have not provided revenue data, had revenues of $109 million. This assumption, the GAO states, may result in a significant overstatement of the reseller's revenue, resulting in a much lower revenue-to-complaint ratio for that offender.

LCI International Inc., the sixth largest long distance carrier in the United States, has also expressed concern over the manner in which the FCC calculates yearly slamming rates to determine top offenders. Unlike the GAO, LCI claims that the FCC's current practice of dividing the number of slamming complaints by a company's annual telecommunications revenue favors larger carriers. This occurs, LCI states, because the larger a company's revenue the more consumers it can slam without appearing to be a major offender. LCI recommends that the FCC calculate its slamming rate ratio by dividing the number of slamming complaints bythe number of new long distance customers, a methodologythat LCI feels is more reflective of company behavior.

LEGISLATION IN THE 105TH CONGRESS

H.R. 2112 (Franks)

A measure to amend the Communications Act of 1934 to increase the forfeiture penalty for telephone service slamming and to require providers of such service to report slamming incidents, and for other purposes. Introduced July 8, 1997; referred to Committee on Commerce.

H.R. 2120 (DeFazio)

A measure to amend the Communications Act of 1934 to strengthen and expand the procedures for preventing the slamming of interstate telephone service subscribers, and for other purposes. Introduced July 9, 1997; referred to Committee on Commerce.

H.R. 3050 (Dingell)

A measure to establish procedures and remedies for the prevention of fraudulent and deceptive practices in the solicitation of telephone service subscribers, and for other purposes. Introduced November 13, 1997; referred to Committee on Commerce.

H.R. 3749 (Bass)

A measure to amend the Communications Act of 1934 to improve the protection of consumers against slamming by telecommunications carriers, and for other purposes. Introduced April 29, 1998; referred to Committee on Commerce. Referred to Subcommittee on Telecommunications, Trade and Consumer Protection May 8, 1998.

H.R. 3888 (Tauzin)

A measure to amend the Communications Act of 1934 to improve the protection of consumers against slamming by telecommunications carriers, and for other purposes. Introduced May 14, 1998; referred to Committee on Commerce. Passed Telecommunications Subcommittee, as amended, by voice vote, August 6, 1998. An amendment in the nature of a substitute offered by Rep. Tauzin was adopted by voice vote by the Commerce Committee, on September 24, 1998. Reported out of committee October 8, 1998 (H.Rept. 105-801). Passed House by voice vote, with amendment, October 12, 1998. Received in the Senate October 13, 1998.

H.R. 4176 (Markey)

A measure to amend the Communications Act of 1934 to protect consumers against 'spamming', 'slamming', and 'cramming', and for other purposes. Introduced June 25, 1998; referred to Committee on Commerce.

S. 1051 (Campbell)

A measure to amend the Communications Act of 1934 to enhance protections against unauthorized changes of telephone service subscribers from one telecommunications carrier to another, and for other purposes. Introduced July 22, 1997; referred to Committee on Commerce, Science, and Transportation.

S. 1137 (Durbin)

A measure to amend section 258 of the Communications Act of 1934 to establish additional protections against the unauthorized change of subscribers from one telecommunications carrier to another. Introduced July 31, 1997; referred to Committee on Commerce, Science, and Transportation.

S. 1410 (Reed)

A measure to amend section 258 of the Communications Act of 1934 to enhance the protections against unauthorized changes in subscriber selections of telephone service providers, and for other purposes. Introduced November 7, 1997; referred to Committee on Commerce, Science, and Transportation.

S. 1618 (McCain)

A measure to amend the Communications Act of 1934 to improve the protection of consumers against slamming by telecommunications carriers, and for other purposes. Introduced February 9, 1998; referred to Committee on Commerce, Science, and Transportation. Passed Commerce Committee, as amended, by voice vote March 12, 1998. Reported out of committee May

5, 1998 (S.Rept. 105-183). Passed Senate (99-0), with amendment, May 12, 1998.

S. 1740 (Collins)

A measure to amend the Communications Act of 1934 to improve protections against the unauthorized change of subscribers from one telecommunications carrier to another, and for other purposes. Introduced March 10, 1998; referred to Committee on Commerce, Science, and Transportation.

LEGISLATION IN THE 106TH CONGRESS

S. 58 (Collins)

A bill to amend the Communications Act of 1934 to improve protections against telephone service "slamming" and provide protections against telephone billing "cramming", to provide the Federal Trade Commission jurisdiction over unfair and deceptive trade practices of telecommunications carriers, and for other purposes. Introduced January 19, 1999; referred to Committee on Commerce, Science, and Transportation.

S. 1084 (McCain)

A bill to amend the Communications Act of 1934 to protect consumers form the unauthorized switching of their long distance service. Introduced May 19, 1999; referred to Committee on Commerce, Science, and Transportation.

FOR ADDITIONAL READING

Federal Communications Commission. Common Carrier Bureau. *Common Carrier Scorecard.* November 1998. Washington, DC. Available at the FCCs Web site: [http://www.fcc.gov/Bureaus/Common_Carrier/Reports/score_card_98.html]

Federal Communications Commission. Common Carrier Bureau. *The FCC Telephone Consumer Complaint Scorecard.* December 1998. Washington DC. Available at the FCC's web site: [http://www.fcc.gov/Bureaus/Common_Carrier/Reports/tccsc98.pdf]

United States General Accounting Office. *Telecommunications: State and Federal Actions to Curb Slamming and Cramming.* GAO/RCED-99-193. July 1999. Washington, DC. Available at the GAO's web site: [http://www.gao.gov]

United States General Accounting Office. *Telecommunications: Telephone Slamming and Its Harmful Effects.* GAO/OSI-98-10. April 1998. Washington, DC. Available at the GAO's web site: [http://www.gao.gov]

Chapter 2

TELEPHONE BILLS: CHARGES ON LOCAL TELEPHONE BILLS[*]

James R. Riehl

SUMMARY

Telephone bills are becoming more and more complex and such change and complexity occasion congressional and regulatory attention as well as constituent requests for explanation of new charges on their bills. As local telephone companies provide additional caller services and continue to act as billing agents for long-distance and information service providers, a customer's local bill can include charges for myriad options that did not exist a few years ago. Bills may now contain charges labeled federal subscriber line charge, presubscribed interexchange carrier charge, "national access fee," "carrier line charge," "federal universal service charge," or local telephone number portability. In addition, customers may now receive bills for different telecommunications services from different telecommunications service providers.

In the past, long-distance companies usually billed business customers directly and residential customers through a local phone company. Recently, long-distance companies have begun billing residential customers directly. One bill has become two. Cellular telephone and personal communications

---
[*] Excerpted from CRS Report RL 30052 Reprted on May 2, 2003.

services (PCS) providers, competitive local exchange carriers (CLEC), and paging companies usually send bills directly to the consumer. Some cable television companies are providing local telephone service, and those charges may appear on a cable bill.

Although surveys show that consumers prefer one readable and understandable bill, there is no federal regulation or law that dictates the layout or wording that is used on bills. This report lists and describes the possible basic charges that commonly appear on most local service telephone bills and discusses the practice of "cramming," the appearance of unauthorized and possibly illegal charges on telephone bills. An overview of various actions by the Federal Communications Commission is also provided.

TELEPHONE COMPANIES

According to estimates of the Federal Communications Commission (FCC), there are over 1,300 companies that provide local telephone services and over 700 companies that provide long-distance telephone services in the United States.[1] There may be almost that many ways of presenting a telephone bill to a customer. The FCC does not dictate the form or wording of a telephone bill. State public utility commissions, the entities that oversee telephone industry regulation within each state, generally do not try to control form and wording of telephone bills either. A collection of FCC Fact Sheets concerning various telephone industry issues is available at [http://www.fcc.gov/cgb/information_directory.html] and also at [http://www.fcc.gov/cgb/telephone.html].

COALITION FOR AFFORDABLE LOCAL AND LONG-DISTANCE SERVICES (CALLS)

In August 1999, six of the largest phone companies (AT&T, Sprint, Bell Atlantic, BellSouth, SBC, and GTE) announced an industry plan to

---

[1] U.S. Federal Communications Commission, *Statistics of* Communications *Common Carriers*, 2001/2002 ed., Washington, 2001, pp. iii-iv. Available via the FCC Web site at [http://www.fcc.gov/wcb/iatd/socc.html].

substantially revise the complicated system of telephone access charges,[2] which include the subscriber line charge (SLC, see the section Subscriber Line Charge) and the presubscribed interexchange carrier charge (PICC, see the section Presubscribed Interexchange Carrier Charge). The plan, referred to as CALLS, was modified by the coalition of phone companies after criticism from the FCC and consumer groups. The FCC adopted the main provisions of this 5-year access reform plan on an interim mandatory basis on May 31, 2000.[3] The access charge rate structure is mandatory for all major local phone companies with certain rate level components being mandatory on an interim basis. The mandatory nature of the plan has been criticized by some companies who do not believe that the plan does enough to guarantee affordable local telephone service in rural, high-cost areas. The plan permits some companies to opt out after the first year. Those who opt out will be subject to special cost studies. Some major long-distance and local telephone companies that were not parties to the proposal and certain consumer groups have criticized the plan. US West, recently acquired by Qwest and the only large local phone company that did not agree to the CALLS plan, and the National Association of State Utility Consumer Advocates (NASUCA) both filed petitions in court for review of aspects of the CALLS plan. US West believed the plan was "arbitrary, capricious and otherwise contrary to law." NASUCA representatives stated that the plan would actually raise phone bills. On September 19, 2000, Qwest altered its position concerning CALLS and agreed to carry out its provisions. Qwest also announced that it would drop various lawsuits that it had filed and would review others.

ACCESS CHARGES

Subscriber Line Charge (SLC)

The subscriber line charge is a federally regulated charge that first appeared on phone bills following the divestiture of the American Telephone & Telegraph Company (AT&T) in 1984. It is also referred to as an "access charge" and is intended to allow local telephone companies to recover some

---

[2] Access charges are the fees that long-distance companies pay to local telephone companies for access to the local phone network
[3] U.S. Federal Communications Commission, *In the Matter of Access Charge Reform...*, FCC 00-193, adopted May 31, 2000, released May 31, 2000. Available via the FCC Web site at [http://www.fcc.gov].

of the fixed costs (telephone wires, poles, and other facilities) of connecting phone customers to the interstate long-distance network. When a customer makes an interstate long-distance call, in the vast majority of cases he/she must use a local phone company's network to connect to the long-distance network. Access charges are paid to local telephone companies by both the end user (business or residential customers) and the long-distance company carrying a long-distance call. The SLC paid by end users appears on a bill as a specific itemized charge. The long-distance company that carries an individual long-distance call pays access charges to both the local phone company originating the call and the one terminating the call. The access charges paid by the long-distance carriers do not appear on a telephone bill. Over the past few years, the FCC reduced the amount of access charges paid by long-distance companies. Access charges are kept by the local phone companies. They are not forwarded to the federal government. Information on the subscriber line charge is provided at the FCC Web site [http://www.fcc.gov/cgb/telephone.html].

In conjunction with decisions related to the implementation of the Telecommunications Act of 1996, the FCC revised the SLC for residential and business customers with more than one telephone line, although SLC charges for customers with a single line did not change. In most cases, until the CALLS revisions, the SLC for a primary residential line was $3.50 per month. Any additional residential lines are considered non-primary lines. The SLC for non-primary lines was capped at $5 per line per month through 1998. Starting in 1999, the SLC for non-primary residential lines was adjusted for inflation and increased $1. It was capped at $6.07. However, this did not mean that all non-primary lines incurred a $6.07 charge on a telephone bill. If the local telephone company's average interstate costs of providing that line were less than $6.07, it could only charge the actual amount of its costs to a consumer.

CALLS Revisions of the SLC

As of July 1, 2000, the SLC and PICC for **residential and single line businesses** were consolidated into a new SLC. The PICC charge was eliminated as a separate charge. The new primary line residential and single-line business SLC was capped at $4.35 per month and on July 1, 2001, rose to $5. Under this plan, the cap was scheduled to rise to $6 on July 1, 2002, and to $6.50 on July 1, 2003. The increases after 2001 are subject to FCC validation. The FCC noted that, for the first year, the new single SLC charge was lower than the separate SLC and PICC charges combined.

The SLC cap for residential customers and single-line businesses remained at $3.50 for smaller local telephone companies (approximately 1,300 carriers providing service to less than 10% of total telephone access lines). On October 11, 2001, the FCC adopted an order to reform these charges also.[4] In this order, referred to as the MAG (Multi-Association Group) Plan, the SLC caps for the smaller carriers were increased to the same levels paid by most other telephone subscribers. As of January 1, 2002, the SLC cap for residential and single-line businesses increased to $5. Beyond that date, the FCC will conduct cost review studies, and the cap may increase to $6 on July 1, 2002, and to $6.50 on July 1, 2003.

2002 and 2003 Increases in the Subscriber Line Charge.

On June 5, 2002, the FCC, following a cost review proceeding, determined that the scheduled increases in the subscriber line charge were appropriate and necessary to fulfill the Commission's access charge reform plans.[5] As a result, as of July 1, 2002, the subscriber line charge cap for residential and single-line business customers increased to $6, and will increase to $6.50 on July 1, 2003. The FCC noted that raising the cap does not mean that all customers will necessarily see a charge at the cap level on their bill. If a phone company's cost of providing the line is less than the cap, it may only recover that actual cost. The cap is the maximum charge that may appear on a bill and applies to all carriers. In order to ensure the affordability of phone service for low-income consumers, the FCC expanded the Lifeline support program, part of the universal service mechanism, to cover the full amount of SLC charges.

Under the CALLS plan, **non-primary line residential** (two or more lines in the home) SLC charges were increased and capped at $7 beginning July 1, 2000. The charge will remain at this level for 5 years. However, if the telephone company's average interstate costs of providing the line are less than $7, it may only charge the customer the amount of its costs. Not all non-

---

[4] U.S. Federal Communications Commission, In the Matter of Multi-Association Group Plan for Regulation of Interstate Services of Non-Price Cap Incumbent Local Exchange Carriers and Interexchange Carriers, FCC 01-304, adopted Oct. 11, 2001, released Nov. 8, 2001. Available via the FCC Web site at [http://www.fcc.gov].

[5] U.S. Federal Communications Commission, *In the Matter of Cost Review Proceeding for Residential and Single-Line Business Subscriber Line Charge (SLC) Caps*, FCC 02-161, adopted June 4, 2002, released June 5, 2002. Available via the FCC Web site at [http://www.fcc.gov].

primary residential lines will be charged at the $7 cap. Prior to the implementation of CALLS, this charge was capped at $6.07, but was scheduled to increase by $1 plus an amount for inflation on July 1, 2000.

In the MAG Plan, the FCC adopted the MAG proposal to apply the same SLC caps to primary and non-primary residential lines of the smaller carriers. The FCC stated that several commenters in this proceeding indicated that higher SLC rates for non-primary lines would limit the growth of these lines, which are often used for advanced telecommunications services and are an important source of revenue for the smaller carriers.

Prior to CALLS, the maximum SLC for **businesses with multiple lines** was $9 per line per month through 1998. In 1999, the multiple line business SLC was adjusted for inflation and increased to $9.20 per line. This charge was adjusted for inflation annually. As with the residential SLC, local phone companies could only recover their costs. Thus, business customers with multiple lines did not necessarily see a $9.20 charge for each line. The amount could be less, and according to the FCC, the average SLC for businesses with multiple lines was $7.17. As a result of the adoption of the MAG Plan order, the multiple line SLC cap for smaller carriers increased to $9.20 on January 1, 2002.

Multiple line businesses will not see a consolidation of the PICC and SLC charges. Under the CALLS plan, the multiple line business PICC is capped at $4.31 (its pre-CALLS cap) and will be reduced and eliminated in most areas over the next several years (or sooner). The multiple line business SLC will be frozen for 5 years. For business customers of the largest local phone companies, the SLC charge is $9.20 or the company's average interstate cost of providing the line in that state, whichever is less. Multiple line business customers of the smaller local telephone companies will be charged $6 or the cost of providing the line in that state, whichever is less. The FCC plans to reevaluate the multiple line business charges at the end of the 5-year period covered by the CALLS plan.

The presence of a cap does not mean that every customer will be charged that specific amount on their bill. The cap is the maximum charge that may appear. The actual charge on an individual phone bill may be lower than the cap.

Presubscribed Interexchange Carrier Charge (PICC)

The PICC began appearing on telephone bills in January 1998. It was a flat-rate per-line charge that long-distance companies paid to local telephone companies. It was charged in addition to the SLC, because the FCC determined that the SLC did not allow local phone companies to recover all of the fixed costs associated with the interstate portion of the local loop. The FCC set PICC charges as ceilings, not absolute rates, and thus specific PICCs varied from state to state depending upon the costs of providing service within the state. The charge could be assessed for all telephone lines regardless of whether a business or residential customer had actually selected (presubscribed) a specific long-distance company.

As of July 1, 1999, the PICC for primary residential lines and businesses with a single line was capped at $1.04 per month, up from $0.53 in 1998. The primary line and single line business PICC was adjusted annually for inflation and increased by $0.50. Through June 30, 2000, the maximum PICC charge for non-primary residential lines was $2.53 per line per month, up from $1.50 in 1998. The cap for business customers with multiple phone lines was raised to $4.31 per line per month, up from $2.75 in 1998. The multiple business line PICC ceiling could be adjusted for inflation and increased, if necessary, by approximately $1.50 per year. As with the residential and single-line business PICC, the FCC estimated that, as its plans were implemented, PICC charges would decrease and eventually reach zero in many places.

Long-distance companies took various approaches to including or not including PICC charges on phone bills. In some cases, the charges appeared as an itemized line on a bill, but they also may have been lumped in with other charges and labeled "national access fee" or "carrier line charge." The FCC did not order long-distance companies to present PICC charges in a specific way, nor did the FCC order the companies to charge the customer directly for PICC charges. The FCC stated that its reductions in access charges which the long-distance companies pay to local phone companies largely offset any increases in per-line or other charges, making them revenue-neutral. Some long-distance companies chose to recover all or part of the PICC charges from their customers and stated that they had to do so because their costs rose and the FCC reductions in access charges were not enough and had already been passed on to customers. Long-distance companies requested further reductions of these charges.

CALLS Revisions of the PICC

Under the CALLS plan, on July 1, 2000, the PICC charge was eliminated as a separate charge for **residential and single line business** customers. The PICC and SLC (see section "Subscriber Line Charge") were consolidated into a single, new SLC charge. However, multiple line businesses will not see a consolidation of the PICC and SLC charges. The multiple line business PICC will be capped at $4.31 (its pre-CALLS cap) and will be reduced and eliminated in most areas over the next several years (or sooner). As with SLC caps, the presence of a PICC cap does not mean that all customers will be charged at the cap rate. The specific charge may be less than the cap and must be based on the actual cost of providing phone service in each area.

Other CALLS Provisions

Overall, according to the FCC, this action will simplify charges and reduce the fees appearing on monthly bills, especially for low-volume residential and business users. Due to the wide variety of billing formats, the different fees on telephone bills, charges attached to different calling plans, and the volume of calls a customer makes, it is not possible to state that any particular bill will decrease by a specific amount or percent. The FCC has stated, however, that low-volume users (30 minutes or less of long-distance calling per month) may save between $10 and $50 per year. Various observers believe it is even more difficult to quantify savings for heavy users of long-distance services. In addition, this action by the FCC may result in an increase in local and long-distance competition and further reductions in long-distance charges.

According to the FCC, some of the major consumer benefits of the CALLS plan are as follows:

- the elimination of the residential and single line business PICC. The multiple line business PICC will be reduced over time and eliminated in some areas.
- a $3.2 billion reduction in access charges paid by long-distance companies to local phone companies.

Although major long-distance companies have agreed to pass these savings on to their customers over the 5-year life of the CALLS plan, some consumer groups and analysts question whether all of the savings would actually reach consumers, and when. The government cannot force the companies to pass on the savings. It is not clear at this time whether per minute charges for long-distance calling will fall.

- availability of at least one long-distance plan (to AT&T and Sprint customers) that does not have a monthly minimum use charge.

Monthly minimum use fees (see the section "Minimum Use Fees") of approximately $3 per month have been charged by some long-distance carriers to customers who do not make large volumes of long-distance calls. Although this plan does not abolish the use of minimum monthly fees and the FCC did not reach the conclusion that such flat fees were unreasonable, inequitable, or inconsistent with the Communications Act, companies agreed to eliminate or make avoidable some of these fees.

As part of the CALLS proposal, AT&T and Sprint agreed to make long-distance plans available that would address the needs of low-volume users. Also, members of the coalition agreed to work with the Consumer Information Bureau at the FCC to develop a consumer education plan. The plan will address important issues relating to long-distance and local phone service pricing and service. In addition, the CALLS companies will create programs and materials to assist consumers in understanding their telephone bills. In order to reach the maximum number of consumers, the materials must be available in various formats and languages. Within 90 days of publication of provisions of the Order in the *Federal Register*, CALLS companies had to submit a compliance statement relating to their consumer education plan to the FCC.[6] Education efforts must continue over the 5-year life of the plan. A report was filed with the FCC on September 19, 2000.

As part of the education effort, the CALLS member companies established Web sites to provide phone bill assistance and other information to consumers. See [http://www.phonebillcentral.org] and [http://www.life linesupport.org/li/lls/].

- identification of $650 million in implicit universal service support and establishment of an explicit universal service support mechanism to replace the implicit support.

According to the FCC, phone companies were collecting approximately $650 million in universal service (see the section "Universal Service") support for high-cost customers through their access charges. Under the new rules, this money is removed from access charges and replaced with an assessment on all telecommunications carriers' interstate revenues. The money will be placed in a new universal service mechanism (separate from

---

[6] *Federal Register*, June 21, 2000, pp. 38684-38704.

the existing high-cost fund) and made available to any carrier serving customers in high-cost areas. This new mechanism is capped at $650 million and is targeted to density zones and study areas that have the greatest need for it. As of July 1, 2000, price cap local phone companies must create a separate line item to recover all contributions to the universal service support mechanism.

For more information on the CALLS plan and its provisions, consult the FCC Web site at [http://www.fcc.gov] or contact them at:

> Federal Communications Commission Consumer and Governmental Affairs Bureau 445 12th Street, S.W.
> Washington, D.C. 20554
> Call toll free: 1-888-CALL-FCC (1-888-225-5322)

TRUTH-IN-BILLING AND BILLING FORMAT

On September 17, 1998, the FCC adopted a Notice of Proposed Rulemaking addressing the issue of the clarity of telephone bills.[7] The three main proposals of the rulemaking were as follows:

- Telephone bills should be clearly organized and highlight any new charges or changes to consumers' services;
- Telephone bills should contain full and non-misleading descriptions of all charges and clear identification of the service provider responsible for each charge; and
- Telephone bills should contain clear and conspicuous disclosure of any information consumers need to make inquiries about charges.

The FCC received over 60,000 consumer inquiries concerning telephone bills in 1998. On April 15, 1999, the FCC issued an Order generally adopting the proposed principles and minimal, basic guidelines to help consumers understand their telephone bills.[8] The guidelines adopted implement three basic principles. Consumers should know:

---

[7] *Federal Register*, Oct. 14, 1998, pp. 55077-55083.
[8] U.S. Federal Communications Commission, *In the Matter of Truth-in-Billing and Billing Format,* First Report and Order and Further Notice of Proposed Rulemaking, CC Docket 98-170, FCC 99-72, adopted Apr. 15, 1999, released May 11, 1999. Available via the FCC Web site at [http://www.fcc.gov].

- who is asking them to pay for service;
- what services they are being asked to pay for; and
- where they can call to obtain additional information about the charges appearing on their telephone bill.

The FCC chose to adopt broad, binding principles instead of detailed rules that would rigidly control all of the wording and the format of a telephone bill. Thus, telephone companies have wide latitude to satisfy the adopted principles in a way that serves the needs of the carrier and the customer. In its Order, the FCC states that:

> "We incorporate these principles and guidelines into the Commission's rules, because we intend for these obligations to be enforceable to the same degree as other rules. Thus, while we provide carriers flexibility in their compliance, we fully expect them to meet their obligation to provide customers with the accurate and meaningful information contemplated by these principles."

Deniable and Non-Deniable Charges

The Truth-in-Billing Order also requires companies to identify charges on a customer's bill that are "deniable" and "non-deniable." Generally, deniable charges are those that, if not paid, may result in the termination (denial) of a customer's local telephone service. Non-deniable charges are those that, if not paid, will not result in termination of the customer's local telephone service. No specific format on a bill is required, although deniable and non-deniable charges must be clearly and conspicuously identified. In addition, carriers are free to choose other methods of informing consumers about charges that may be contested. State laws may also address this issue.

The FCC views identification of charges into these two categories as protecting consumers from paying questionable, unauthorized charges out of fear of having their local telephone service disconnected. However, this guideline applies only to companies who include both categories of charges on a single bill. Companies that bill directly for a service that includes no basic local telephone service would not be covered. For example, customers being billed directly by a wireless telephone company for only wireless service would not have charges for wired basic local telephone service on their bills. Although not paying charges on the wireless bill would have no effect on their at-home wired service, non-payment of the wireless bill may result in termination of their wireless service.

Essentially, customers should not conclude that every bill for a telephone service has both deniable and non-deniable charges on it. Prior to withholding payment for any charge on a bill, a customer should verify the status of the charge with the billing company.

After reviewing petitions for reconsideration relating to truth-in-billing and billing format, the FCC on March 29, 2000, released an Order on Reconsideration that reaffirmed the requirement that telephone bills highlight new service providers and prominently display a contact number for inquiries. This requirement is intended to act as a deterrent to slamming and cramming by allowing consumers to more easily identify changes in providers on their bills. The rule does not cover services provided on a per-transaction basis like directory assistance. Changes in a customer's local or long-distance company would be covered.[9]

The Order also adopted proposals to require carriers to use standard industry-wide language and clear descriptions for line item charges identified as resulting from federal regulatory activity. The FCC felt that current presentations of these charges on telephone bills are misleading, inaccurate, and confusing. As a result, through a proceeding announced in the *Federal Register*, the FCC will seek comment from consumer and industry groups concerning standard labels for these charges.[10]

Finally, carriers must prominently display on each bill a toll-free number (or numbers) that customers may use to inquire about or dispute any charge on their bill.

Provisions of this Order not subject to further rulemakings become effective 30 days after the publication of notice of the effective date in the *Federal Register*. That notice was published in the October 12, 1999 *Federal Register* on pages 55163-55164. All other principles and guidelines adopted in the Order became effective on November 12, 1999.[11]

The FCC provides consumer information on truth-in-billing, charges on telephone bills, and other telephone issues at their Web site. See [http://www.fcc.gov/cgb/phonebills/samplePhonebill.html], [http://www.fcc.gov/cgb/information_directory.html], and [http://www.fcc.gov/cgb/telephone.html].

Complaints concerning telephone service may be filed via the FCC Web site at [http://www.fcc.gov/cgb/complaintfiling.html].

---

[9] *Federal Register*, July 13, 2000, pp. 43251-43258.
[10] *Federal Register*, June 25, 1999, pp. 34499-34501.
[11] A summary of this Order was published in the *Federal Register* on June 25, 1999, on pages 34488-34498.

State regulatory authorities may also address telephone billing formats and customer service practices of telephone companies operating in their state.

CHARGES ON LOCAL TELEPHONE BILLS

Local Telephone Service

This is the basic amount that a customer pays for local dialing service, not including any taxes or additional services. State public utility commissions regulate this charge, not the FCC. For Web connections to state public utility commissions, see the National Association of Regulatory Commissioners Web site at [http://www.naruc.org/resources/state.shtml].

Table 1. Average Residential Rates for Local Service in Urban Areas, 1995-2001

	1995	1996	1997	1998	1999	2000	2001
Monthly Charge	$13.62	$13.71	$13.67	$13.75	$13.77	$13.64	$14.05
Subscriber Line Charge	3.54	3.54	3.53	3.52	3.58	4.50	5.03
Touch-Tone Service Charge	.44	.30	.25	.10	.09	.06	.06
Taxes, 911, and Other Charges	2.41	2.40	2.42	2.39	2.48	2.57	2.70
Total	**$20.01**	**$19.95**	**$19.88**	**$19.76**	**$19.93**	**$20.78**	**$21.84**

Source: *Reference Book of Rates, Price Indices, and Household Expenditures for Telephone Service*, by Keith Brown, Federal Communications Commission, July 2002. Available at [http://www.fcc.gov/wcb/iatd/stats.html].

Notes: Figures are average rates as of October 15, 2001, for flat-rate calling in a sample of 95 cities. Separate charges for touch-tone service are no longer levied in 81 of the cities, but have been incorporated into the basic monthly charge. Charges for add-on services, such as caller ID, call forwarding, etc., and cellular services are not included in the table.

The geographic size of a local dialing area and the structure of local dialing service packages vary from company to company and from state to state. Typically, customers may have local telephone service that allows an unlimited number of calls *within* their local dialing area for a flat monthly fee or a service package that allows up to a specific number of local calls during any one month. If a customer exceeds that number of calls, the extra calls are subject to additional charges. Usually, the various local telephone service plans are summarized in the front section of the white pages of a telephone book. In many cases, companies providing local telephone service list the individual component charges that are included in the fee a customer pays for local service. Questions concerning any of these components or the fees charged for each component should be addressed to the company providing local phone service or the state public utility commission. The FCC does not establish or regulate local plan prices or components.

Table 2. Representative Local Rates for Businesses with a Single Line in Urban Areas, 1995-2001

	1995	1996	1997	1998	1999	2000	2001
Monthly Charge	$32.48	$32.58	$32.76	$32.44	$32.41	$32.18	$31.97
Subscriber Line Charge	3.57	3.54	3.54	3.54	3.52	4.39	4.99
Touch-Tone Service Charge	.97	.82	.38	.32	.25	.19	.18
Taxes, 911, and Other Charges	4.79	4.87	4.99	4.97	5.03	5.04	5.04
Total		$41.81	$41.81	$41.67	$41.27	$41.21	$41.80	$42.18

Source: *Reference Book of Rates, Price Indices, and Household Expenditures for Telephone Service*, by Keith Brown, Federal Communications Commission, July 2002. Available at [http://www.fcc.gov/wcb/iatd/stats.html].

Notes: Figures are as of October 15, 2001. The monthly charge presented in this table is a "representative rate." Since flat-rate calling was available for single-line businesses in only 54 of the 95 cities in the survey, the FCC used the measured/message service rate (along with charges for placing 100 5-minute, same-zone, business-day calls) in combination with flat-rate charges to calculate a representative rate. No add-on services or cellular charges are included. Additional business tables are available in the FCC report cited.

Table 3. **Average Household Expenditure for Telephone Service (All Households), 1994-2000**

	1994	1995	1996	1997	1998	1999	2000
Annual Household Expenditure for Telephone Service	$690	$708	$772	$809	$830	$849	$877
As a Percent of Total Household Expenditures	2.17%	2.19%	2.28%	2.32%	2.34%	2.29%	2.31%
Household Expenditure per Month	$57.50	$59.00	$64.33	$67.42	$69.17	$70.75	$73.08

Source: *Reference Book of Rates, Price Indices, and Household Expenditures for Telephone Service*, by Keith Brown, Federal Communications Commission, July 2002. Available at [http://www.fcc.gov/wcb/iatd/stats.html].

Note: Statistics obtained from U.S. Bureau of Labor Statistics surveys of consumer expenditures. Charges for add-on services, such as caller ID and cell phone services, are included in these statistics. Data presented in the FCC report cited.

Directory Assistance Charges

Local phone companies, in most cases, assess charges for directory assistance (411) calls. Rates can be as high as $1.25 per call. Charges for 411 calls are not regulated by the FCC. State authorities may regulate these charges. In some states, there are extensive regulations. In other states, the phone companies are given more freedom in assessing 411 fees. Local phone companies may allow a certain number of calls per month to 411 without charging any fee. Above that number, fees are assessed. Customers seeking to avoid these charges should contact their local phone company and ask about the number of free calls that may be permitted; use a phone book; try the Internet; or call a friend to get a number.

Inside Wiring

In some cases, a charge labeled "Inside Wiring" may appear on a customer's bill. This is an *optional* charge that customers may pay to a company for service calls on the wiring *inside* their home. Monthly fees for inside wiring "insurance" vary from company to company. Inside wiring is owned by the home or building owner.

Customers paying this fee are not charged any additional monies if the company is requested to repair inside wiring. Customers choosing not to pay this fee will be charged by the phone company for any necessary inside wiring repairs requested. Fees charged for inside wiring work vary from company to company. If a customer has an inside wiring problem, there is no requirement to call the phone company. Since the wiring is owned by the home or building owner, any company may be called or the owner may choose to work on the wiring.

Toll Calls

Each telephone customer is permitted (within the parameters of their local dialing plan) to call certain telephone exchanges in their geographic area without incurring any additional charge on their telephone bill. Because of the introduction of new area code overlays, local telephone calls may require seven-digit or 10-digit dialing. Calls made *outside* of a customer's local dialing area, but not going far enough to be classified as long-distance, will incur additional charges on a telephone bill. Local dialing areas are not determined by the FCC. State authorities regulate the local dialing areas in their state and make the determination as to whether calls to certain exchanges are within a specific local dialing area or are toll calls.

Toll calls are often handled by the same company that provides local telephone service to a customer. However, in many states, state authorities have permitted long-distance carriers to compete in the toll call market. Toll call rates can vary substantially depending upon the carrier chosen (in states where such competition is permitted) and other factors. If there are any questions concerning toll call charges or whether a specific exchange is included in a local dialing area, they should be addressed to the company providing local telephone service or state authorities.

In-State Connection Fee

Long-distance companies may have a charge on a bill labeled the In-State Connection Fee or something similar. According to the long-distance carriers, this is a fee to recover the charges that local telephone companies assess on the long-distance companies to carry in-state long-distance and toll calls over their lines. These charges are often referred to as intrastate access charges. The FCC does not regulate the fee assessed to recover these charges. Customers with questions about the fee on their bill or intrastate access charges should contact the companies involved and their state public utility commission.

In some cases, long-distance companies exempt certain customers from the fee. For example, customers who have certain service packages from the long-distance company, customers enrolled in certain types of lifeline programs, or customers who spend less than $1 per month on long-distance calling.

Jamming

With the advent of competition in the toll call market, complaints have arisen that some customer accounts are being frozen so that customers cannot use a company competing with their local phone company to complete a toll call. This tactic is referred to as jamming. In cases where this is occurring, customers may be paying more for their toll calls. Customers who feel that they have been jammed and have inquiries about competition in the toll call market should address their inquiries to state authorities.

Sliding

Some customers have also complained that their chosen provider of toll call service has been switched without their permission. This practice has been termed sliding. As with jamming, toll call rates can vary substantially from company to company. Consumers who believe that they have been victims of sliding should contact their chosen toll call provider or state authorities.

Miscellaneous Caller Services

Local telephone companies offer a wide variety of caller services such as: caller ID, call waiting, call forwarding, call rejection, call trace, call return, priority ringing, and voice mail, among many others. Both the types of caller services offered and the charges for these optional services vary from company to company. Charges may include monthly fees or per-use charges. The FCC does not regulate these charges.

Long-Distance Services

Long-distance charges are wholly dependent upon the long-distance company that a consumer chooses as his/her long-distance carrier, the particular calling plan (if any) chosen, and the number and length of calls made during a billing period. Usually, customers designate a specific long-distance company as their primary long-distance carrier. When a customer dials a long-distance call by dialing 1+(area code)+telephone number, a telephone switch automatically routes the call to the customer's designated long-distance carrier. However, customers are not required to use their designated long-distance carrier to handle any of their long-distance calls. If customers use "dial around" long-distance carriers (reached by dialing the appropriate 10-10-XXX code for a particular company) instead of their chosen long-distance carrier, charges for those calls can also be included on a local bill. In addition, customers may use different types of pre-paid phone cards or long-distance company calling cards to complete a long-distance call. Rates and conditions for these cards vary widely, and the charges billed to a card can vary depending upon whether a payphone, business, or residential phone is used.

Many long-distance companies are now billing their residential customers directly instead of billing through a local telephone company. As a result, customers may receive a minimum of two bills for telephone service.

On March 1, 2000, the FCC and the Federal Trade Commission (FTC) issued a joint *Policy Statement* concerning advertising practices relating to long-distance services, especially dial-around (10-10) numbers.[12] The agencies took this action following thousands of complaints from consumers

---

[12] Joint FCC/FTC Policy Statement For the Advertising of Dial-Around And Other Long-Distance Services To Consumers, Policy Statement, File No. 00-72, FCC 00-72, released Mar. 1, 2000.

and issued the *Statement* to "... encourage industry to adhere to the standards offered in the joint Policy Statement." According to the FCC and FTC, the *Policy Statement* does not preempt any existing state law.

Suggested guidelines for advertising of long-distance services are as follows:

- All claims must be truthful, non-misleading, and substantiated;
- Carriers should disclose all costs consumers may incur, such as per-call minimum charges, monthly fees, and universal service charges;
- Advertising should disclose any time or geographic restriction on the availability of advertised rates;
- The basis for comparative price claims should be disclosed, and only current information used in making claims; and
- Information should be disclosed in a clear and conspicuous manner, and without distracting elements, so that consumers can understand it and make fully informed choices.

Consumers are usually charged a fee of up to $5 by a local telephone company when they change the long-distance carrier selected as their primary carrier. Often, the newly designated long-distance carrier will pay the fee as an incentive to obtain new customers. The fee has been capped at $5 since the 1984 divestiture of AT&T. On March 14, 2002, the FCC began a proceeding to examine this charge.[13] The agency will seek to determine if the charge is outdated and may, in fact, hinder competition by discouraging consumers from switching companies. As part of the proceeding, the FCC will attempt to determine whether it should set a lower cap or rely on market forces to set reasonable rates.

The FCC provides Consumer Fact Sheets at its Web site, see [http://www.fcc.gov/cgb/information_directory.html] or [http://www.fcc.gov/marketsense/welcome.html] or [http://www.fcc.gov/cgb/consumerfacts/longdistance_detariff.html].

Single Bill Fees

Customers who receive a single bill for local and long-distance services may be charged a fee by the long-distance company for this service. The fee is not mandated by the FCC and is not a federal charge. In some cases,

---

[13] *Federal Register*, May 15, 2002, pp. 34665-34669.

customers are informed in advance about the fee. In other cases, no advance notice is given. Should this charge appear on a phone bill, a customer must contact their long-distance company and inquire about separate billing for long-distance calls. The fee will then not apply. Single bill fees are approximately $1.50 per month. An FCC Fact Sheet is available at [http://www.fcc.gov/cgb/consumerfacts/singlebill.html].

Slamming

Generally, slamming is the unauthorized change of a customer's long-distance service provider.[14] There are existing FCC rules and policies designed to protect telephone customers from this practice, and sections of the Telecommunications Act of 1996 prohibit carriers from changing a customer's long-distance company without following specific verification procedures. On April 13, 2000, the FCC adopted additional rules to combat slamming.[15] As a result, state regulatory agencies will be responsible for resolving slamming disputes. In cases where a state elects not to administer the slamming rules, the FCC will resolve disputes. The new rules also require slammers to compensate both the consumer and the authorized carrier.

Consumers may verify the long-distance carrier connected to their home phone by calling 1-700-555-4141 *from their home phone*. A recording will state the name of the long-distance carrier connected to that line. This is an automated service. Consumers cannot call the 700 number from another location to verify service on their home phone. Calls must be made from the line for which one wishes to verify service.

If there is a problem, customers should contact their local telephone company and chosen carrier and arrange to be switched back to the chosen carrier at no charge. If there was a charge for switching or higher rates when slammed, customers have the right to demand a refund. Consumers may also choose to contact their state's Attorney General, public utilities commission, or a consumer protection group or agency.

The FCC provides information on telephone slamming at its Web site at [http://www.fcc.gov/cgb/consumerfacts/slamming.html]. Complaints concerning slamming may be filed electronically at the FCC's Consumer

---

[14] For an overview of the slamming issue, see CRS Issue Brief IB98027, *Slamming: The Unauthorized Change of a Consumer's Telephone Service Provider*, by Angele A. Gilroy.
[15] *Federal Register*, Aug. 3, 2000, pp. 47678-47693.

Information Bureau Web site [http://www.fcc.gov/cgb/complaintfiling.html]. Complaints may also be filed directly with the FCC:

> Federal Communications Commission Consumer and Governmental Affairs Bureau 445 12th Street, S.W.
> Washington, D.C. 20554
> Call toll free: 1-888-CALL-FCC (1-888-225-5322)

Minimum Use Fees

Certain long-distance carriers charge minimum use fees to some of their long-distance customers. In most cases, basic rate customers (those customers who are not on any calling plan) are assessed the charge. However, in some circumstances, customers on calling plans may also be charged. The companies stated that it was necessary to assess the charge because of the expenses of billing, account maintenance, and customer service. Consumer advocates condemned the charge as punishing low volume callers. The fee, if assessed, can be $3 or more per month.

Long-distance carriers may exempt qualifying low-income customers from paying the fee and, usually, long-distance calls made during the month are applied against the fee. If a customer makes $2.50 in long-distance calls during the month, 50 cents will be added to the bill to bring charges up to the $3 minimum. If calls exceed $3, there is no additional fee. Questions about the structure of these fees or company policies concerning the fees should be directed to a customer's long-distance carrier.

Consumers should note that a minimum use fee is different from the monthly charge that may be assessed by a particular company's calling plan. A customer might pay $5.95 per month to be on a plan that offers long-distance rates of 10 cents per minute, 24 hours per day. This charge does not increase or decrease regardless of the volume or cost of calls made during the billing period.

Customers who wish to avoid minimum use charges may contact their long-distance carrier and inquire about discount calling plans, switch to a long-distance company that does not charge minimum use fees, or cancel their designated long-distance carrier. Most long-distance calling plans, regardless of the company, may carry basic monthly charges. These charges often exceed $3. Should a customer cancel the designated long-distance carrier, they will still receive *incoming* long-distance calls, but would only be able to make *outgoing* long-distance calls by using dial-around carriers, prepaid calling cards, or cell phones. Customers choosing this option should pay strict attention to the details of the price structure of dial-around or prepaid services. Prices for these methods vary significantly.

CALLS Revisions

Neither the FCC nor the states currently regulate minimum use fees charged by long-distance companies. On July 9, 1999, the FCC announced that it would begin an inquiry into how these fees affect low volume callers.[16] This inquiry was concluded as part of the CALLS proposal adopted on May 31, 2000 (see section "Coalition for Affordable Local and Long-Distance Services"). Although minimum use fees were not abolished, companies agreed to eliminate them or make these fees avoidable through special calling plans with no minimum monthly charge.

The FCC provides a series of tips at their Web site for choosing a long-distance provider. See [http://www.fcc.gov/marketsense/welcome.html].

Internet Access and Long-Distance Charges (Reciprocal Compensation)

Members of Congress and the FCC have been inundated with inquiries concerning the classification of telephone calls to Internet Service Providers (ISP) as long-distance instead of local. Those complaining believed that Congress and the FCC were about to enact provisions that would make all calls to ISPs subject to long-distance charges. There were and are no bills in Congress to do this.

The FCC conducted a proceeding at the request of telephone carriers to clarify how local telephone companies should compensate each other (reciprocal compensation) for carrying telephone traffic to ISPs. Essentially, when Telephone Company X (a local phone provider) delivers a local call to the ISP, who has chosen Telephone Company Z to handle its local calls, X pays Z to deliver the call to the ISP. If the ISP calls someone, Z pays X to deliver the call. Charges paid from X to Z or Z to X are based upon the length of time that the call is connected or some other basis determined by X and Z. X and Z enter into an agreement for a specified period of time to compensate each other for carrying calls. This compensation is paid between X and Z and does not involve any charges to the ISP or its customers and has no direct bearing on the fees that an ISP charges its customers.

---

[16] *Federal Register*, Aug. 5, 1999, pp. 42635-42637.

However, calls to ISPs tend to last a long time, since using the Internet is usually not a speedy endeavor, but outbound calls from ISPs do not (in most cases). Thus, local phone companies like X end up paying a lot more to Z than Z pays to X since the compensation is often based upon the length of time that the call is connected. X and other local phone companies in the same position petitioned the FCC to reconsider the status of these calls and designate them as interstate instead of local. Reciprocal compensation applies only to local telephone calls.

On February 25, 1999, the FCC ruled that "... Internet traffic is jurisdictionally mixed and appears to be largely interstate in nature" and in a Notice of Proposed Rulemaking is seeking to determine a federal inter-carrier compensation mechanism.[17] Designation of these calls as interstate by the FCC is a purely jurisdictional designation. Although this ruling means that the structure and method of reciprocal compensation (payments between X and Z) will change, it does not change the status of local calls to ISPs to long-distance for the purposes of billing individual customers. It also does not require an end to reciprocal compensation. The U.S. Court of Appeals for the District of Columbia ruled, on March 24, 2000, that the FCC had not adequately justified its analysis of phone calls to Internet service providers as interstate. The case was sent back to the FCC for further explanation.

In an Order released on April 19, 2001,[18] the FCC concluded that telecommunications traffic delivered to ISPs is interstate access traffic and is not subject to reciprocal compensation. However, the FCC did not abolish reciprocal compensation. Instead, it established a gradual reduction of the rates over the 2 years following the effective date of the order.

The FCC does not regulate the fees that ISPs charge their customers for Internet access. ISPs construct their own packages of monthly, weekly, hourly, or per-minute charges for their customers. Additional information is available via the FCC Web site at [http://www.fcc.gov/Bureaus/Common_ Carrier/Factsheets/nominute.html].

---

[17] *Federal* Register, Mar. 24, 1999, pp. 14203-14206, 14239-14243.

[18] U.S. Federal Communications Commission, *In the Matter of ... Intercarrier Compensation for ISP-Bound Traffic*, Order on Remand and Report and Order, CC Dockets 96-98 and 99-68, FCC 01-131, adopted Apr. 18, 2001, released Apr. 27, 2001. Available via the FCC Web site at [http://www.fcc.gov].

Federal Telephone Excise Tax

The federal telephone excise tax first appeared in 1898 as a temporary tax to finance the Spanish-American War. The tax reappeared in 1914 as a tax on long-distance service necessitated by World War I. It has been repealed and reinstated several times since then. The tax was made permanent by the Revenue Reconciliation Act of 1990 (P.L. 101-508) and is currently assessed at a rate of 3% on local and long-distance telephone services. Monies collected from this tax are not kept by the telephone companies but are forwarded to the U.S. Department of the Treasury for general revenue purposes.[19] The Telecommunications Act of 1996 (P.L. 104-104) did not alter this tax. Legislation to repeal this tax was introduced, but did not become law, in the 106th Congress. Similar legislation has been introduced in the 107th Congress.

Telephone excise tax collections have been as follows: FY2001 ($5.7 billion), FY2000 ($5.6 billion), FY1999 ($5.2 billion), FY1998 ($4.8 billion), FY1997 ($4.7 billion), and FY1996 ($4.2 billion).

Because charges on a telephone bill are presented in numerous ways, it is not always clear to what amount the 3% federal excise tax is applied. Essentially, the tax is assessed on all local and long-distance telephone services. According to the IRS code (section 4251), the tax is imposed on "...amounts paid for communications services...." Communications services are defined as including local telephone service, toll telephone service, and teletypewriter exchange service.

Many telephone bills may have a line labeled "federal tax" or "federal excise tax" with an amount next to it, but the total upon which the tax is based may not appear near the federal tax line. To determine the total upon which the tax is based, perform the following calculation:

If the federal excise tax on a bill is listed as $1.21.
$1.21 is 3% of what number?

$1.21 \div .03 = 40.3333$

---

[19] For additional information on the telephone excise tax, see CRS Report RS20119, Telephone *Excise Tax* and CRS Report RL30553, *The Federal Excise Tax on Telephone Service: A History*, both by Louis Alan Talley.

The total upon which the 3% federal excise tax was calculated was $40.33. That total may appear somewhere else on the bill, or the individual components that add up to the total may be presented.

Excise Tax on Frequent Flier Miles

Some long-distance companies offer their customers the chance to earn frequent flier miles based on their long-distance calling plan. The long-distance companies purchase the miles from airlines and award them to their customers according to the rules of the promotion being offered. Congress, in the Taxpayer Relief Act of 1997, established an excise tax of 7.5% on the purchase of frequent flier miles. The airlines collect the tax from the companies that purchase the miles. Some long-distance companies have chosen to pass all or part of this tax on to their customers who receive the miles. They are free to do so, but are not required to do so. Although the long-distance companies collect this charge via the telephone bill, it is not a telephone-related charge and although the charge is the result of a federal excise tax, it is not related to the 3% federal telephone excise tax mentioned above.

Local Number Portability (LNP)

The Telecommunications Act requires implementation of local number portability. LNP permits telephone customers to retain their telephone number even if they switch telephone companies. LNP was implemented in stages and was initially available in the 100 largest metropolitan areas. Phone companies reportedly have spent approximately $3 billion to implement LNP.

As of February 1, 1999, local phone companies may, but are not required to, assess a monthly charge on customers' telephone bills to recover some of their costs incurred in implementing LNP. A monthly charge for LNP may appear on customers' bills only in areas where LNP has been implemented. The charge will vary from company to company and region to region depending upon the costs incurred to implement LNP. According to various reports, LNP charges that have been assessed have been in the 20 to 60 cents range. In most cases, residential and business customers will be charged the same amount. The charge is permitted to continue for 5 years from the date it first appears, but should not increase during that time.

Since LNP was implemented in stages, customers in the largest metropolitan areas will probably saw the charges first, while customers in other areas will not see any charge until LNP is implemented in their area. Any carrier assessing an LNP end user charge must file a tariff with the FCC. On July 1, 1999, following a 5-month investigation, the FCC announced that it had directed several local phone providers to reduce their charges for LNP. According to the FCC, this action will result in a savings of $584 million to consumers.

Wireless and competitive local exchange carriers (CLEC) and long-distance companies have also incurred costs associated with LNP. These companies are not subject to the same restrictions regarding cost recovery and are free to charge their customers as much or as little as they want over a period of time of their choice to recover the costs associated with LNP implementation. As a result, customers may see wireless, CLEC, and long-distance companies assessing an LNP charge also.

Wireless Local Number Portability

The wireless telephone industry and the FCC are in the process of implementing LNP for wireless customers. As a result of technical problems, implementation has been delayed. Under current FCC rules, wireless LNP is scheduled to be in place by November 24, 2003.

Universal Service

Section 1 of the Communications Act of 1934, as amended, states that one of the reasons for creation of the FCC is to

> "... make available, so far as possible, to all the people of the United States, without discrimination on the basis of race, color, religion, national origin, or sex, a rapid, efficient, Nation-wide, and world-wide wire and radio communication service with adequate facilities at reasonable charges ..."

The Telecommunications Act of 1996 added section 254 (Universal Service) to the Communications Act. This section states that policies for the preservation and advancement of universal service shall be based upon, among other things, quality service at just, reasonable, and affordable rates and that access to advanced telecommunications and information services should be available in all regions of the nation.

The concept of universal service can trace its roots to the turn of the century and the early years of the telephone system in the United States. During these years, a complex system of cross subsidies developed to fund telephone services for all citizens of the United States. Wiring rural areas was much more expensive than wiring urbanized population centers. Profits generated in the urbanized areas were used to subsidize rural wiring. Higher rates were charged for business customers and long-distance calls, enabling lower residential charges for local calling. Later, assistance was provided for low-income households. As the years passed, revenues continued to increase, and these complex cross subsidies enabled the funding of universal service at affordable rates for all citizens.

With the divestiture of AT&T in 1984, the expansion of competition, and advances in technology, the structure of the telecommunications industry in the United States began a complex transformation that continues today. No longer was the system of cross subsidies applicable mainly to a single major provider of telephone service. At divestiture, seven "Baby Bells" were created. Due to mergers and corporate restructuring, only four of the original seven remain, and only one of those has the same name it had at divestiture. The number of local and long-distance providers mushroomed, and the country entered the information age. Telephone service was no longer limited to a wired connection in a home or business. New questions arose relating to the concept of universal service. What type of connections should be included? Who should contribute to a universal service mechanism? How much should they pay? How should they pay?

As a result of the Telecommunications Act of 1996, the FCC attempted to answer some of these questions. In its May 7, 1997, universal service and access reform decisions, the agency, in compliance with the provisions of the 1996 Act, expanded the field of entities eligible for universal service to include schools and libraries (known as the "E-rate"[20]) and rural health care providers. The pool of companies paying to fund universal service was enlarged and access charges were restructured.

Up until the present time, telephone bills for the most part did not include itemized charges for universal service. While, technically, all telephone customers have contributed to universal service for decades, such

---

[20] For more detailed information on the E-rate, see CRS Issue Brief IB98040, Telecommunications Discounts for Schools and Libraries, and CRS Report 98-604, E-Rate for Schools: Telecommunications Discounts Through the Universal Service Fund.

charges were built into the rate system. The companies that currently pay into the universal service mechanism do so based upon their revenues and a quarterly contribution factor, not according to a specific fee. The FCC had not established rules mandating or forbidding phone companies from itemizing their universal service costs on telephone bills, and there is no specific federal universal service charge that must be charged directly to customers. Phone companies are taking different approaches to itemizing universal service costs on customers' bills. Some phone companies feel that they must pass on the costs of universal service directly to their customers and are itemizing charges on bills to reflect this. Any charge on a phone bill labeled as a "federal universal service charge" or "universal service connectivity charge" or something similar has been added as a specific item by the company issuing the bill. Questions about any such charges should first be directed to that company.

There has been a great deal of consumer confusion over universal service charges presented on telephone bills. Some companies collect a flat monthly fee. Other companies assess the charge as a percentage of the interstate portion of the bill. The flat fees and the percentages vary from company to company. Telecommunications providers pay a percentage of their interstate end-user revenues into the universal service mechanism based on a contribution factor that is adjusted quarterly. The contribution factor, as of the second quarter of 2003, is set at 9.0044%.[21] Some companies that assess the universal service fee based on a percentage have assessed the charge at percentages exceeding 10%. Many consumers have complained about charges exceeding the contribution factor claiming that the companies are profiting from collecting excessive universal service fees. Telecommunications companies have stated that they are only recovering the universal service fee and administrative and other business costs associated with collecting the fee.

On May 8, 2001, the FCC initiated a review of the way that telecommunications carriers contribute to the universal service fund. Part of the review will be to ensure that the carriers' contributions are recovered (from customers) fairly, accurately, and equitably. In a *Federal Register* notice published on March 13, 2002, the FCC invited additional comments on reforming the universal service contribution recovery process to make it more fair and understandable for consumers.

---

[21] Information on the quarterly contribution factor is available at the FCC Web site at: [http://www.fcc.gov/wcb/universal_service/quarter.html].

2003 Changes in Universal Service Fees on Phone Bills

Following a review of the comments received by the FCC, the Commission announced new rules on December 13, 2002, that prohibit telecommunications carriers who choose to recover universal service contribution costs through a line item on telephone bills from assessing universal service fees that exceed their universal service fee contribution factor. If the contribution factor is 9%, the line item on the phone bill may not exceed 9%. The carriers may continue to choose to express the line item as a flat fee or as a percentage, as long as the charge does not exceed the total amount associated with the contribution factor. Although this action should result in lower universal service fees for many consumers, the FCC did not prohibit the carriers from recovering their administrative and other costs through their customer rates or another line item. Those additional costs, however, may not be included in the universal service fee on the phone bill. In addition, carriers may not recover universal service contributions from Lifeline (qualifying low-income) customers. The rules take effect on April 1, 2003.[22] The FCC chose not to direct the carriers to use specific wording to label the universal service line item on a phone bill. As a result, language is likely to vary. A summary of the FCC action may be found in the *Federal Register* on December 30, 2002, on pages 79525 through 79533.

For extensive information on the FCC's actions relating to universal service and copies of documents see [http://www.fcc.gov/wcb/universal_ service/welcome.html], as well as the FCC Consumer Fact Sheets on universal service at [http://www.fcc.gov/cgb/information_directory.html].

The universal service fund is administered by the National Exchange Carrier Association (NECA), which can be reached via their Web site [http://www.neca.org] or at:

National Exchange Carrier Association
80 South Jefferson Road
Whippany, NJ 07981-1009
(800) 228-8597

---

[22] U.S. Federal Communications Commission. *In the Matter of Federal-State Board on Universal Service ... and Truth-in-Billing and Billing Format*, FCC 02-329, adopted Dec. 12, 2002, released Dec. 13, 2002. Available via the FCC Web site at [http://www.fcc.gov].

NECA's subsidiary, the Universal Service Administration Company (USAC), provides detailed information on the various components of the universal service mechanism at [http://www.universalservice.org].

Local Taxes

The county, city, or state in which an individual lives often has its own tax on telephone service. Local taxes may be much higher than the federal excise tax and can exceed 20%. Local taxes may include: franchise, gross receipts, state sales, local sales, municipal, special district, or earnings taxes, and state mandated universal service surcharges.[23] Some or all of these charges may appear on a customer's telephone bill. Questions about these taxes should be directed to local phone companies, state public utility commissions, or local tax authorities.

Property Taxes

In some cases, a telephone company may include a charge on the bill to recover the property taxes that it pays to local governments. It may be called the Carrier Property Tax or something similar. Assessing this charge on a customer is the company's choice. The FCC does not regulate this practice, and it is not a federal tax.

Interstate Tax Surcharge

This charge, also known as a gross receipts tax, applies to interstate revenues generated by long-distance telephone companies within an individual state. It is not a federal tax. State or local tax authorities can provide information on this tax.

911 Charges

Local government authorities are responsible for the construction and maintenance of 911 emergency calling systems within a state. Any 911

---

[23] Telecommunications Tax Policies: Implications for the Digital Age, National Governors' Association, Feb. 2000.

charges or taxes appearing on a bill are dependent upon a local government's actions relative to 911 and will vary from locale to locale. Implementation of an enhanced 911 (E911) system is underway for wireless service providers. As a result, customers of cellular and personal communications services and other wireless service companies may see 911 charges on their bills.

Relay Center Surcharges

Also known as Telecommunications Relay Services (TRS), this charge is used to provide operator-assisted telecommunications services for people with hearing or speech disabilities. Costs for intrastate TRS services are paid by the states. Costs for interstate TRS services are borne by the Interstate TRS fund, administered by the National Exchange Carrier Association and funded by all interstate carriers. The NECA collects funds from approximately 3,000 companies based on their interstate revenues. Charges on customers' bills are usually a few cents per telephone line. TRS services are required by Title IV of the Americans With Disabilities Act (P.L. 101-336). For additional information on TRS, see the FCC's Web site at [http://www.fcc.gov/cgb/dro/trs.html] and [http://www.fcc.gov/cgb/consumerfacts/trs.html].

Cramming

Customers who cannot determine what a specific charge is for might have been "crammed." Cramming refers to the inclusion of unauthorized or possibly illegal charges that appear on a customer's bill. An amount might be labeled as "monthly fee," "membership," or "information service." Contact should be made with the local telephone company or bill provider to obtain the name, address, and phone number of the company for whom they are collecting the fee in question. Consumers should request that the charge be removed from the bill if they believe they are a victim of cramming. Since the local phone company is usually only acting as a billing agent for a company, they cannot resolve individual disputes. However, they should be made aware of the situation.

Complaints concerning questionable charges for calls placed within a customer's state should be directed to a local consumer office or the state public utility commission and the company that initiated the charge in question.

If the charges involve information services (900 numbers, psychic hotlines, etc.), not telephone services, a customer may register a complaint with and obtain information from the FTC Web site [http://www.ftc.gov] or:

Federal Trade Commission Consumer Response Center,
Room 130 600 Pennsylvania Avenue,
N.W. Washington, D.C. 20580
Toll free: (877) 382-4357

Should the complaint involve telephone-related issues, interstate or international services, or charges, a complaint may be registered in writing with the FCC:

Federal Communications Commission Consumer and Governmental Affairs Bureau 445 12th Street, S.W.
Washington, D.C. 20554
Call toll free: 1-888-CALL-FCC (1-888-225-5322)

The FCC is currently conducting an inquiry into invalid and unclear charges on telephone bills. The FCC provides further information at its Web site, [http://www.fcc.gov/cgb/consumerfacts/cramming.html].

Information on the FCC's anti-cramming best practices guidelines is provided at [http://www.fcc.gov/Bureaus/Common_Carrier/Other/cramming/cramming.html].

Internet Cramming

Recently, a cramming scam that targets small businesses, religious groups, charities, foundations, or any small organization desiring an Internet presence has generated thousands of complaints. Companies, usually through some type of telemarketing[24] operation, will contact consumers and offer a "free trial" for the design and maintenance of a Web site. In many cases, such companies fail to disclose that, unless the free trial is specifically canceled by the consumer, a monthly fee (for continued maintenance of the Web site) will be collected and charged to a customer's telephone bill. In some cases, even when the free trial is canceled by the customer, the charges continue to appear on the customer's phone bills.

The FTC has filed Internet cramming cases against various companies and provides information at their Web site. Complaints may be filed at the FTC Web site or by contacting the FTC at the address or phone number listed above.

CHARGES ON WIRELESS TELEPHONE BILLS

Many of the charges that appear on local (wired) telephone bills also appear on bills issued by wireless companies. Most notably: monthly service charges, itemized call charges (local and long-distance, depending upon the calling plan a customer chooses), federal telephone excise tax, 911 fees, any applicable state or local taxes, universal service charges, LNP, and TRS fees. As with local phone bills, wording used on wireless bills can vary from company to company. Also, wireless companies are not subject to the same truth-in-billing and billing format principles discussed earlier in this report. However, the FCC is currently conducting an inquiry into whether its truth-in-billing requirements should apply to wireless carriers and what uniform labels should be used to identify charges resulting from federal action.[25]

Neither SLC nor PICC charges appear on wireless bills. However, some wireless companies use the wording "Interconnect/Landline Charges," or "Landline Connection Fee" on their bills. This charge is not a result of the FCC access charge mechanism. It is a charge assessed by a local phone company to connect a wireless call through their network to the called party. The charge varies company to company and calling plan to calling plan.

Although many charges on wireless bills are similar to or the same as those on wireline bills, there is a series of charges that are particular to wireless. For instance, wireless customers in many cases are billed for both incoming and outgoing calls, and wireless companies may start billing for a call as soon as the send button is pressed. Unlike wireline calls, a charge may appear on a wireless bill for a call that did not go through. In addition, wireless companies often bill by the minute, not by the second. As a result, a call lasting 61seconds may be billed as a two minute call. Also, there may be substantial termination fees assessed on customers who try to cancel their service before a certain date, and there are usually geographic limits for coverage provided by different companies and plans.

---

[24] For more detailed information on telemarketing, see CRS Report RL30763, *Telemarketing: Dealing with Unwanted Telemarketing Calls*, by James R. Riehl.
[25] *Federal Register*, June 25, 1999, pp. 34499-34501.

The FCC has no regulatory authority over these various fees or billing practices. Essentially, when customer signs up for wireless telephone services, they have entered into a contractual agreement with a company. Customers must read the contract carefully and fully understand the terms. The monthly charge quoted for service is not necessarily the full cost of a calling package. Just as with wireline telephone bills, fees and surcharges added to a bill can substantially increase the base price of a monthly plan. Labels and names attached to these fees and surcharges vary significantly. In cases where customers believe they have been misled or have been the victims of some questionable business practice or incorrect charge, they may wish to contact the office of the attorney general or the public utility commission in their state. The FCC provides information on wireless phone bills and issues at [http://www.fcc.gov/cgb/phonebills/WirelessPhone bill.html] and [http://www.fcc.gov/cgb/cellular.html].

FEDERAL COMMUNICATIONS COMMISSION

The FCC Consumer Information Bureau has developed a Web site devoted to various telephone-related issues. The site includes several FCC fact sheets on specific telephone-related issues and summaries of enforcement actions, and it allows consumers to file complaints electronically.
See [http://www.fcc.gov/cgb/information_directory.html].

Federal Communications Commission Consumer and Governmental Affairs Bureau 445 12th Street, S.W.
Washington, D.C. 20554
Call toll free: 1-888-CALL-FCC (1-888-225-5322)

The FCC Web site provides a list of main, complaint, and in-state, toll-free telephone numbers for the telecommunications regulatory authorities in each state. The list is available at [http://www.fcc.gov/wcb/iatd/state _puc.html]. No mailing addresses are provided.

NATIONAL ASSOCIATION OF REGULATORY UTILITY COMMISSIONERS

The National Association of Regulatory Utility Commissioners (NARUC) is an organization of state and federal regulatory commissioners having jurisdiction over public utilities. Individual state public utility commissions (PUC) may provide assistance to consumers concerning telephone bills and any state laws and regulations that may apply to companies providing telephone services within the state.

Web site connections and addresses for state PUCs are available through the NARUC Web site at [http://www.naruc.org]. Also, NARUC can be contacted at the following address:

National Association of Regulatory Utility Commissioners
1101 Vermont Avenue, N.W., Suite 200
Washington, D.C. 20005
(202) 898-2200

Chapter 3

FCC DEVELOPMENTS AND FAQ CONCERNING SLAMMING[*]

Federal Communications Commission

SLAMMING

"Slamming" is the illegal practice of changing a consumer's telephone service - local, intralata service, or interlata service (including state to state, in state and international long distance) - without permission. The Commission's slamming liability rules provide a remedy if you've been slammed and take the profit out of slamming for telephone companies. The FCC's Enforcement Bureau will also take action against slammers. These rules apply to slamming violations that occur on or after November 28, 2000. (For slamming violations that occurred before that date, you can still file a complaint with the Commission. See information telephone number listed below.)

What Are Your Rights If You Have Been Slammed?

You may file a complaint with the relevant state agency or with the FCC (see below).

---

[*] Excerpted from http://www.fcc.gov/slamming/

If you find that you have been slammed, and you have NOT paid the bill of the carrier who slammed you:

- You do not have to pay anyone for service for up to 30 days after being slammed, neither your authorized telephone company (the company you actually chose to provide service) nor the slamming company.
- You must pay any charges for service beyond 30 days to your authorized company, but at that company's rates, not the slammer's rates.

If you **HAVE** paid your phone bill and then discover that you have been slammed:

- The slamming company must pay your authorized company 150% of the charges it received from you.
- Out of this amount, your authorized company will then reimburse you 50% of the charges you paid to the slammer.
- For example, if you were charged $100 by the slamming company, that company will have to give your authorized company $150, and you will receive $50 as a reimbursement.
- The subscriber also has the option of asking the authorized carrier to re-rate the unauthorized carrier's charges.

With these rules, the Commission has taken the profit out of slamming and protected consumers from illegal charges.

What Can I Do If I've Been Slammed?

If your telephone company has been changed without your permission:

- If you choose to call the slamming company to request that the problem be fixed, and you have not yet paid, tell the slamming company that you will not pay for the first 30 days of service.
- Call your authorized company (local or long distance) to inform them of the slam. Tell them that you want to be reinstated to the same calling plan you had before the slam. Tell them that you want all "change of carrier charges" (charges for switching companies) removed from your bill.

FCC Developments and FAQ Concerning Slamming

- File a complaint with the appropriate government agency. *See the next section.*

How do I File a Complaint?

See if your state is listed below. If it is, these states and commonwealths have agreed to handle your complaint.

Alabama	Louisiana	New Jersey	Utah
Arkansas	Maine	New York	Vermont
California	Maryland	North Carolina	Washington
Colorado	Massachusetts	North Dakota	Wyoming
Connecticut	Michigan	Ohio	District of Columbia
Florida	Minnesota	Oklahoma	
Idaho	Mississippi	Oregon	Puerto Rico
Indiana	Montana	South Carolina	
Iowa	Nebraska	South Dakota	
Kansas	Nevada	Tennessee	
Kentucky	New Hampshire	Texas	

If your state is **not** listed above, then send an e-mail or written complaint to the FCC. Here is the address:

Federal Communications Commission
Consumer & Governmental Affairs Bureau
445 12th Street S.W.
Washington, DC 20554
E-mail: slamming@fcc.gov

Be sure to include this information:

- your name, address and phone number
- phone number that was slammed
- your email address
- name of the phone company that slammed you
- name of your authorized local phone company
- name of your authorized long distance company
- a complete statement of the facts

- COPIES of your phone bill showing the charges that you are disputing **(Important: if you file using e-mail, your bill must be attached, electronically, to your e-mail. Otherwise, you must file by letter and attach paper copies of your bill)**
- whether or not you have paid any of the disputed charges
- the specific relief that you want.

Still Have Questions?

For futher information contact the FCC's Consumer Center at 1-888-CALLFCC (voice) or 1-888-TELLFCC (TTY).

FCC ANNOUNCES EFFECTIVE DATE OF REVISED SLAMMING LIABILITY RULES

Rules Become Effective on November 28, 2000
CC Docket No. 94-129

The Common Carrier Bureau of the Federal Communications Commission (FCC) announces the effective date of the slamming liability rules adopted by the FCC in its First Order on Reconsideration in the slamming proceeding, *Implementation of the Subscriber Carrier Selection Changes Provisions of the Telecommunications Act of 1996* and *Policies and Rules Concerning Unauthorized Changes of Consumers' Long Distance Carriers*, CC Docket No. 94-129, FCC 00-135 (rel. May 3, 2000). The revised slamming liability rules will take effect on November 28, 2000.

"Slamming" is the unauthorized change of a consumer's preferred telecommunications carrier. In the First Order on Reconsideration, the FCC responded to certain petitions for reconsideration of its Second Report and Order, 14 FCC Rcd 1508 (rel. December 23, 1998), by modifying the slamming liability rules and refining the procedures for administering those rules.

Summary of Slamming Rules

Under the revised procedures, states will be able to "opt in" to become the primary forums for administering the slamming liability rules and resolving slamming complaints. If a state has not opted in, the FCC will resolve slamming complaints filed by the citizens of that state.

The strengthened slamming liability rules take the profit out of slamming and increase the incentives for authorized carriers to go after slammers. The rules also ensure that, if the FCC or the state commission finds that a slam occurred, the consumer will receive compensation. Where the consumer has not paid the unauthorized carrier, the consumer will be absolved of the obligation to pay for service for up to 30 days after a slam. Where the consumer has paid the unauthorized carrier, the rules require the unauthorized carrier to pay 150% of the charges it received from the consumer to the authorized carrier, which must, in turn, reimburse the consumer 50% of the charges paid by the consumer.

The Federal Register published a summary of the First Order on Reconsideration on August 3, 2000. 65 FR 47678. The revised liability rules adopted in the order contained information collections, which the Office of Management and Budget approved on October 3, 2000. OMB No. 3060-0787. As stated in the order, notice of the November 28, 2000 effective date will be published in the Federal Register.

For more information, contact Michele Walters or Dana Walton-Bradford, Accounting Policy Division, Common Carrier Bureau, (202) 418-7400, TTY (202) 418-0484, mwalters@fcc.gov or dwalton@fcc.gov.

WHEN YOUR TELEPHONE SERVICE IS SWITCHED WITHOUT YOUR PERMISSION - "SLAMMING

Background

"**Slamming**" is the illegal practice of changing a consumer's traditional (wired) telephone service without permission. New consumer protection rules created by the Federal Communications Commission (FCC) provide a remedy if you've been slammed.

Your Rights if You Have Been Slammed

If you have been slammed and HAVE NOT paid the bill of the carrier who slammed you:

You DO NOT have to pay anyone for service for up to 30 days after being slammed. This means you do not have to pay either your authorized telephone company (the company you actually chose to provide service) or the slamming com-pany. You must pay any charges for ser- vice beyond 30 days to your authorized company, but at that company's rates, not the slammer's rates.

If you HAVE paid your phone bill and then discover that you have been slammed:

The slamming company must pay your authorized company 150% of the charges it received from you. Out of this amount, your authorized company will then reimburse you 50% of the charges you paid to the slammer. For example, if you were charged $100 by the slamming company, that company will have to give your authorized company $150, and you will receive $50 as a reimbursement.

With these rules, the FCC has taken the profit out of slamming and protected consumers from illegal charges.**New Guidelines for Telemarketing Switches**

Before a telephone company can place an order to switch a customer who agreed to sign up during a telemarketing call, the company must use *at least one of* the following methods to verify that the customer authorized the switch:

- Obtain a written or electronic *Letter of Agency* (LOA) from the customer. Any written or electronic LOA used to confirm a telemarketing order must include: (1) the subscriber's billing name and address, (2) each telephone number to be covered by the order to change the subscriber's telephone company, (3) a statement that the subscriber intends to change from his or her current telephone company to this new company, (4) a statement that the sub- scriber designates this new carrier to act as the agent for this change, and (5) a statement that the subscriber understands that there may be a charge for this change. It must also be separate from any promotional material - like prizes, contests, and forms - that come with it.

- The LOA provided by the carrier must be limited strictly to authorizing a change in telephone carrier and it must be clearly identified as an LOA authorizing the change. The LOA must be written in clear language and the print must be of sufficient size and readable style, generally comparable in type, style, and size to any promotional materials, and must make clear to the consumer that the document, when signed, would change his or her telephone carrier.

Only the name of the telephone carrier that will set the consumer's rates can appear on the letter of authorization. The LOA must also contain full translations if it uses more than one language.

NOTE: Advertising promotions that use checks can incorporate an LOA but must meet specific guidelines. A check must contain the necessary information to make it a negotiable instrument and shall not contain any other promotional language or material. The carrier must place the required LOA language near the signature line on the back of the check. In addition, the carrier must print on the front of the check, in easily readable, bold-faced type, a notice that the consumer's signature will authorize a change in his or her telephone carrier.

Authorized Switching Methods

Be aware that your telephone service cannot be **legally** switched from one company to another unless one of the following methods is used to initiate and verify the switch:

- Your authorization is obtained by a **signed letter** provided by the new company, which indicates, in writing, that you want to switch telephone companies.
- The company must provide a toll-free number that you can call to confirm the order to switch telephone companies.
- The company must have an independent third party verify your oral authorization to switch.

NOTE: The Communications Act makes telephone companies responsible for the acts of their agents, including their telemarketers.

How to Protect Yourself Against Slamming

Be a smart consumer:

- Always examine your phone bill immediately and thoroughly. If you see a new company name on your phone bill, call the number that's shown on that portion of the bill and ask for an explanation.
- Be aware of the ways in which companies are legally permitted to change your telephone service. The FCC's rules require companies to obtain your clear permission before such a change. For example, a company may send you an LOA to verify that you want to switch your service to a new company. The LOA is only valid if you sign and date it. It must be used solely to authorize a change in company, and it must be clearly identified as an LOA authorizing the change. Only sign it when you are sure you want to change companies.

Be firm with telemarketers:

- If you receive a call from a telemarketer about switching your telephone service and you're not interested in changing your service, tell the caller that you're not interested in receiving the services of the company that the telemarketer represents. You can also ask the caller to remove your telephone number from its solicitation lists.

Carefully read all materials you receive in the mail:

- If you receive a letter in the mail from a company asking you to "verify" that you switched telephone services, and neither you nor anyone in hour household authorized the change, immediately notify that company that you did not authorize the switch. Then, immediately call your local telephone company to confirm that you are still with your preferred local, local toll, and long distance company(ies).

Read the fine print in any sweepstakes or drawing entry form before filling it out.

- The form may indicate that by signing it, you've given authorization to switch long- distance companies. In some states, this is illegal and should be reported to that state's Attorney General's Office.

Be careful when answering telephone surveys.

- Be careful of companies conducting surveys. If whoever answers the telephone says "yes" to any of the surveyor's questions, their answers may be taped and used later as verification of authorization to switch long distance companies.

"Freeze" your existing carrier.

- A freeze lets your local phone company know that you do not want to switch providers unless they receive written or verbal authorization from you.

What to Do if You've Been Slammed

If your telephone company has been changed without your permission:

- Call the slamming company and tell them that you want the problem fixed. If you have not paid, tell them that you will not pay for the first 30 days of service. Call the authorized company (local or long distance) to inform them of the slam. Tell them that you want to be reinstated to the same calling plan you had before the slam. Tell them that you want all "change of carrier charges" (charges for switching companies) removed from your bill.
- Be sure to make a note of the names of the employees at each company you spoke with in an effort to resolve your complaint and the dates you spoke with them.
- You can also file a complaint. Depending on where you live, you will either file with your state or with the FCC. There is a list of which states accept complaints at www.fcc.gov/slamming. You can also check with your state's regulatory commission or Attorney General. The number for your state's regulatory commission, Attorney General, or Consumer Affairs Office is in the blue pages (the "State Government" section) of your phone book.

- You can call the following toll-free numbers to verify your phone provider:
    - 1-700-555-4141 for long distance services and
    - 1+your area code+700-4141 for local toll services.

Your state's regulatory commission or Attorney General's Office can advise you on the appropriate procedures for filing complaints with local authorities. In addition, the FCC's Consumer Center at 1-888-CALL-FCC (1-888-225-5322) voice, or 1-888-TELL-FCC (1-888-835-5322) TTY, provides information on slamming and slamming complaints. If your state does not handle slamming complaints, contact the FCC at these numbers for instructions on how to file a complaint with the FCC.

You may file a complaint with the FCC by e-mail (fccinfo@fcc.gov); the Internet (www.fcc.gov/cgb/complaints.html); telephone 1-888-CALL-FCC (1-888-225-5322) voice; or 1-888-TELL-FCC (1-888-835-5322) TTY; or mail: Federal Communications Commission Consumer & Governmental Affairs Bureau Consumer Inquiries and Complaints Division 445 12th Street, SW Washington, DC 20554.

Be sure to include the following information in your complaint:

- your name, address, and phone number;
- the phone number that was slammed;
- your e-mail address;
- name of the phone company that slammed you;
- the name of your authorized local phone company;
- the name of your authorized long distance company;
- a complete statement of facts;
- COPIES of your phone bill showing the charges that you are disputing; (IMPORTANT: If you file using e-mail, your bill must be attached, electronically to your e-mail. Otherwise, you must file by letter and attach paper copies of your bill.)
- whether or not you have paid any of the disputed charges; and
- the specific relief that you want

For More Information

For further information about slamming, visit the FCC's slamming Web site at www.fcc.gov/slamming. For more information about other telecommunications-related subjects, please visit the FCC's Web site at www.fcc.gov/cgb.

In addition, you can contact the FCC's Consumer & Governmental Affairs Bureau at
1-888-CALL-FCC
(1-888-225-5322) voice or
1-888-TELL-FCC
(1-888-835-5322) TTY.

INDEX

A

abuse, 17, 19
access charges, 27, 28, 31, 32, 33, 41, 51
activities, vii, 1, 2, 4
administration, 15, 54
advances, 51
advertising, 42, 43
age, 51
agent, 55, 66
aid, 32
assessment, 33
association, 16
AT&T, 8, 18, 26, 27, 33, 43, 51
authority, 5, 6, 8, 12, 13, 15, 58

B

BellSouth, 26
benefits, 32
best practices, 56
business, 25, 28, 29, 30, 31, 32, 38, 42, 49, 51, 52, 58
business costs, 52

C

cable television, 26
California, 63
change, 1, 44
Columbia, 7, 8, 47, 63
Communications Act, 5, 6, 20, 21, 22, 23, 33, 50, 67
Communications Act of 1934, 20, 21, 22, 23, 50
competition, vii, 1, 3, 4, 18, 32, 40, 41, 43, 51
competitive, vii, 2, 4, 16, 26, 50
competitive local exchange carriers (CLECs), 26, 50
compliance, vii, 2, 6, 8, 9, 33, 35, 51
components, 27, 38, 49, 54
confusion, 16, 52
congress, 2, 3, 4, 11, 12, 14, 15, 16, 17, 19, 20, 23, 46, 48, 49
connectivity, 52
consent, vii, 1, 3, 5
consumers, vii, 1, 2, 3, 4, 5, 7, 8, 9, 10, 11, 12, 15, 16, 17, 18, 19, 20, 21, 22, 23, 26, 29, 32, 33, 34, 35, 36, 42, 43, 50, 52, 53, 56, 58, 59, 62, 66
content, 18
corporate restructuring, 51
costs, 28, 29, 30, 31, 43, 49, 50, 52, 53

credit, 15
customers, 19, 20, 25, 28, 29, 30, 31, 32, 33, 35, 36, 37, 40, 41, 42, 43, 44, 45, 46, 47, 49, 50, 51, 52, 53, 55, 57, 58

D

demand, 44
dependent, 42, 55
development, 3
disclosure, 34
discrimination, 50
divestiture, 27, 43, 51

E

earnings, 54
education, 17, 33
election, 15
email, 63, 64, 70
employees, 16, 69
expenditures, 39

F

federal, 5, 10, 11, 15, 16, 25, 26, 28, 36, 43, 47, 48, 49, 52, 54, 57, 59
Federal Communications Commission (FCC), v, vii, 1, 2, 3, 4, 5, 6, 7, 8, 9, 10, 11, 12, 13, 14, 15, 16, 17, 18, 19, 20, 23, 24, 26, 27, 28, 29, 30, 31, 32, 33, 34, 35, 36, 37, 38, 39, 40, 41, 42, 43, 44, 45, 46, 47, 50, 51, 52, 53, 54, 56, 57, 58, 61, 63, 64, 65, 66, 69, 70, 71
finance, 48
firm, 68
fixed cost, 28, 31
flexibility, 35
Florida, 63
free, 7, 8, 34, 35, 36, 39, 45, 49, 50, 56, 58, 67, 70
freedom, 39
funding, 51
funds, 55

G

government, 9, 69
groups, 27, 32, 36, 56
growth, 17, 30
guidelines, 34, 35, 36, 43, 56, 67
guilty, 13

H

health, 51
health care, 51
House, 13, 14, 15, 16, 21

I

implementation, 2, 3, 16, 19, 28, 30, 49, 50
incentive(s), 18, 43, 65
income, 29, 45, 51, 53
incumbent local exchange carrier (ILEC), 19
industry, vii, 2, 4, 8, 9, 10, 11, 15, 16, 17, 19, 26, 36, 43, 50, 51
inflation, 28, 30, 31
information, 9, 15, 28, 33, 43, 45, 52, 56, 58, 70
insurance, 40
Internet, 2, 7, 9, 11, 39, 46, 47, 56, 57, 70
interstate access, 47
issues, vii, 2, 7, 9, 26, 33, 36, 56, 58

J

jurisdiction, 6, 23, 59

K

Kansas, 63

L

language, 36, 53, 67
law enforcement, 4
laws, 12, 15, 35, 59
legislation, 2, 3, 4, 11, 13, 15, 16, 17, 48
local exchange carriers, 2, 18, 19
local government, 54, 55
long distance, vii, 1, 2, 3, 4, 5, 6, 7, 9, 10, 12, 13, 14, 17, 18, 20, 23, 61, 62, 63, 68, 69, 70
Louisiana, 63

M

management, 65
market, vii, 10, 13, 18, 19, 40, 41, 43
marketing, vii, 1, 3, 12, 13, 15
measures, 2, 3, 4, 11, 16, 17, 19
methodology, 2, 16, 19, 20
minority, 4

N

national, 25, 31, 50

O

organization, 56, 59

P

penalties, 4, 5, 6, 12, 13, 17
Pennsylvania, 56
policy(ies), 4, 10, 11, 17, 19, 42, 44, 45, 50, 65
population, 51

prices, 38, 46
primary, 2, 16, 18, 28, 29, 30, 31, 42, 43, 64
private-sector, 17
procedures, 2, 6, 7, 8, 9, 13, 21, 44, 64, 70
profits, 51
programs, 16, 19, 33, 41
property taxes, 54
punishment, 10

Q

Qwest, 27

R

radio, 50
ranking, 15
recovery, 50, 52
regulation(s), vii, 1, 3, 4, 6, 9, 10, 11, 12, 15, 17, 26, 29, 39, 59
regulators, 2
religion, 50
report, 9, 10, 12, 14, 15, 17, 19, 20, 26, 33, 38, 39, 57
responsibility, 7
revenue, 20, 30, 31, 48
rewards, 6

S

savings, 32, 50
self, 4, 16
Senate, 10, 12, 13, 14, 15, 21, 23
services, vii, 1, 3, 4, 5, 6, 10, 13, 14, 15, 17, 25, 26, 30, 32, 34, 35, 36, 37, 38, 39, 42, 43, 46, 48, 51, 55, 56, 58, 59, 68, 70
Sprint, 26, 33
standards, 15, 43
statistics, 19, 26, 39
study, 9, 10, 14, 34

subscribers, 12, 14, 15, 21, 22, 23, 29
subsidies, 51
summaries, 58
suppliers, vii, 1, 3, 17

52, 53, 54, 55, 56, 57, 58, 59, 61, 62, 65, 66, 67, 68, 69, 70
Texas, 63
trade, 16, 23

T

tariff, 9, 10, 50
tax collection, 48
taxes, 37, 54, 55, 57
technology, 51
telecommunications, vii, 1, 2, 3, 4, 5, 6, 8, 9, 12, 14, 15, 16, 17, 20, 21, 22, 23, 25, 30, 33, 47, 51, 52, 53, 55, 58, 64, 71
Telecommunications Act, vii, 2, 5, 6, 11, 28, 44, 48, 49, 50, 51, 64
telemarketing, 57, 66
telephone, vii, 1, 2, 3, 5, 6, 8, 9, 10, 11, 12, 13, 15, 20, 21, 22, 23, 25, 26, 27, 28, 29, 30, 32, 33, 34, 35, 36, 37, 40, 41, 42, 43, 44, 46, 47, 48, 49, 50, 51,

U

U.S. Department of the Treasury, 48
United States (US), 20, 24, 26, 27, 50, 51

V

voice mail, 42

W

work, 33, 40
World War I, 48